PASSING ON

PASSING ON

❧

DAVID SUDNOW

PRENTICE-HALL, INC., *Englewood Cliffs, N. J.*

Passing On
by David Sudnow

Library of Congress Catalog Card Number: 67-17730

Printed in the United States of America

T 65272

PRENTICE-HALL INTERNATIONAL, INC., *London*
PRENTICE-HALL OF AUSTRALIA, PTY. LTD., *Sydney*
PRENTICE-HALL OF CANADA, LTD., *Toronto*
PRENTICE-HALL OF INDIA PRIVATE LTD., *New Delhi*
PRENTICE-HALL OF JAPAN, INC., *Tokyo*

CONTENTS

❧❦

Preface

This study was undertaken during the years 1963-65, and was originally reported upon in a doctoral dissertation at the University of California, Berkeley. A more extended and analytic presentation of the findings, written for the sociologist, will be published shortly by Prentice-Hall.

Field investigations such as were conducted here would not have been at all possible were it not for the cooperation of those persons both at "County" and "Cohen" hospitals who allowed me to scrutinize their activities and take their time with my questions. In many ways, they made themselves and their work scenes accessible to my research attention. In accord with my promises to them, I cannot thank individuals by name, nor identify the institutions in a locatable way. Without their cooperation, freely given with no concern to hide facts from me or me from them, this book would be much less complete than it now is. For the unquestioning freedom of inquiry given me, I am very grateful.

Several of my sociologist colleagues offered suggestions on ways to improve the study at earlier stages in its preparation, particularly when it was prepared as a doctoral dissertation. I am greatly appreciative of the criticisms and suggestions offered by John Clausen, Harold Garfinkel, Erving Goffman, Helen Pat Gouldner, Andie Knutson, Sheldon Messinger, Harvey Sacks, Emanuel Schegloff and Roy Turner. I am especially indebted to those who arranged partial financial support at various stages in the course of the research: John Clausen, Anselm Strauss, Rodney Coe and Albert Wessen.

Without the editorial help of Jean Reynolds, of Prentice-Hall, which involved the reorganization of much of the manuscript for the current edition, the presentation of the research findings in a readable form would not have been accomplished. In large part it is she who has made this edition possible.

My wife, Elizabeth, contributed in more ways than I could ennumerate to the preparation of the various stages of the manuscript.

A NOTE TO THE READER

To aid the general reader, footnotes have been placed at the end of the book, assembled by reference to chapters. In addition, two appendices containing more extensive considerations of some of the definitional problems I have investigated are included at the end. Those discussions are intended for the reader more interested in the sociological aspects of the problems of "dying" and "death."

This excellent hotel is very ancient. Even in King Clovis' time people died in it in a number of beds. Now they are dying there in 559 beds. Factory like, of course. Where production is so enormous an individual death is not so nicely carried out; but then that doesn't matter. It is quantity that counts. Who cares anything today for a finely finished death? No one. Even the rich, who could after all afford this luxury of dying in full detail, are beginning to be careless and indifferent; the wish to have a death of one's own is growing ever rarer. A while yet, and it will be just as rare as a life of one's own. Heavens, it's all there. One arrives, one finds a life, ready made, one has only to put it on. One wants to leave or one is compelled to; anyway, no effort: Voila, votre mort, monsieur. *One dies just as it comes; one dies the death that belongs to the disease one has (for since one has come to know all diseases, one knows too, that the different lethal terminations belong to the diseases and not to the people; and the sick person has so to speak nothing to do).*

Rilke, The Notebooks
of Malte Laurids Brigge

PASSING ON

I

Death in The Hospital

Death has always been a major topic of human concern. Anthropologists have studied its rituals, physicians and psychiatrists its causes and effects, artists and writers its existential features. With the exception of several recent expositions of American funeral practices, however, death in modern society has not been investigated by sociologists.[1] Nowhere do we have descriptions of how dead bodies are handled in our hospitals, how care is given "dying" patients, how members of deceased patients' families are informed of the deaths of their relatives, how the social organization of the hospital is affected by and affects the occurrence of deaths within its confines.

This book seeks to provide such information. The facts reported here are based on my own observations in two "typical" hospitals—a large, urban, "charity" institution, and a comparable sized, private, general hospital. The former setting will be referred to throughout the book as "County," the latter as "Cohen."

The most extensive field observation was conducted at County, and most of the book will refer to this institution

3

and the place of "dying" and "death" within it. Having obtained what I felt to be a fairly complete view of the County social structure during my nine month stay, I decided to investigate a quite different kind of setting; one where, in contrast to County, private physicians played a prominent role in daily hospital life, and where, unlike County, with its chiefly lower-class patients, the largest proportion of patients were middle and upper-middle class. On occasion, members of traditional "old families" used Cohen Hospital. Approximately five months of field work was done at Cohen, my concern essentially being to provide a comparative basis so as to be able to partially place the observations I had made at County in perspective. My references to practices at Cohen are intended to provide the reader with a sense of the variability in death practices in differing hospital settings.

The study is first and foremost an investigation of death in the county hospital setting. While County is not claimed to be representative of all such organizations, it most definitely appears to be in a class quite distinct from the private hospital. Whether or not findings based on observations at County are applicable to other welfare-based hospitals cannot be presently established, but they do not appear to be applicable to hospitals as a whole. At every point in my investigation I found disparate practices between County and Cohen, not only with respect to the treatment of "dying" patients, but with regard to a wide range of aspects of medical care.

The following tables, taken from hospitals' annual reports summarize some information about the two settings:

TABLE I

Average Daily Census

County	Cohen
370	440

TABLE II

Annual Number of Discharges and Deaths Per Year

	County	Cohen
Discharges	18,000	15,000
Deaths	1,000	425
(%)	5.5	2.8

TABLE III

Average Length of Stay in Acute Divisions, in Days

County	Cohen
6.2	9.1

TABLE IV

Religious Composition of Patient Population

	County	Cohen
Catholic	29%	23%
Protestant	70.4%	45%
Jewish	.5%	31%
Other	.1%	1.0%

TABLE V

Racial Composition of Patient Population

	County	Cohen
White	59%	88%
Negro	40%	12%
Other	1%	—

The two institutions were of similar overall size. However, the social class composition of their patient populations was noticeably different. County was very much a lower-class establishment, and Cohen very decidedly a middle-class institution.

The slightly higher death rate at County (and a 2 per cent differential is considered by physicians as substantial with respect to such matters) is partially explained by the fact that at County there is a very active Emergency Unit, where accident victims are brought by the police department, while the Emergency Room at Cohen is used infrequently. A sizeable proportion of the total number of deaths at County, over 30 percent, occur as the result of accidents, suicides and cases where no period of hospitalization preceded the death. Discounting the influence of the "dead on arrivals" ("DOA") on the total percentages, the two institutions had roughly the same death rates, with only a slightly greater proportion of deaths-per-bed at County.

Over a period of one and a half years, I spent nearly the entire workweek in the hospitals. Although I spent time on all three work shifts at County, most of it was on the day and evening shifts. Access to the hospitals was gained through formal administrative channels, in both instances through the Director of Nursing and the Chiefs of Medicine and Surgery. Personnel at this level were informed that the concern of my research was to investigate how staff members handled the treatment of "dying" patients. On the wards themselves, my own accounts of my purpose ranged from rather detailed discussions, particularly with members of the medical staff, to only casual accounts like "I'm just interested in what you do here." In all, I witnessed approximately 250 deaths.

Initially, my procedure involved the location of those wards in the hospital which, according to daily census reports, had the highest number of deaths. I was introduced, by upper-echelon administrators, to the personnel in charge of these areas, as a "sociologist studying the social organization of the hospital." Gradually, over the course of several weeks, I became acquainted with all members of the staff from orderlies to resident physicians. At County, I was not required to dress as a physician, but wore a business suit except when I was in the Emergency Unit, in surgery or in the delivery rooms. At Cohen, I was asked to wear a resident's gown, which I found had the advantage of making me less subject to queries from staff members, and had the disadvantage of leaving me open to a variety of requests by patients and their families.

The bulk of my time was spent watching and listening. When possible to do so unobtrusively, I took notes in a small book. In other situations I made a practice of recording significant occurrences as soon as I could get to a private place. In each hospital I was given an office, to which I returned repeatedly during the day to write down more extensive records and dictate memos to myself. Only on rare occasions were formal interviews held, and those few which were necessary involved personnel from whom I wanted to gather technical information about hospital procedures.

On various occasions, unsuccessful attempts were made to record actual conversations. With the permission of administrators, tape recorders were placed in concealed locations, and wireless transmitters were carried on my body, but due to the high level of background noise in the hospital setting, only bits and pieces of conversations were transcribed. In the body of the text wherever double quotation marks are used to frame a person's speech, or indentations are made to indicate a quotation, the quotation is as nearly literal as an on-the-spot, handwritten recording would permit. My limited shorthand ability aided somewhat in this recording activity.

In conducting such field work, I have been aware of the possible effect of my own presence on the behavior of participants on the scene. My only claim to its minimal relevance is my feeling that by virtue of my long stay in the hospital, particularly at County, the staff came to take my presence for granted. In the early days of my research at County, I distinctly felt that many staff members monitored their activities to show me what they thought I wanted to see. As I became well-known to the staff and they became less suspect of my intentions, however, I felt sufficiently ig-

nored and had the impression that what I was witnessing
would have gone on were I not around.

Most of my information is based on casual conversations
I had with members of the staff, and more important, on my
observations on the scene. Each morning I made grand
rounds with members of the house staff, engaged them in
conversation and attended their conferences. On special
days I attended various specialty conferences (vascular surgery, cancer clinic, obstetrics rounds, etc.). During the rest
of my day I spent most of the time standing about nurses'
stations, overhearing conversations in corridors, following
physicians as they treated their patients, witnessing surgical,
obstetrics and autopsy procedures, sitting in waiting rooms
and cafeterias, chatting with members of families and the
like. In both settings I was free to go where I pleased, and
in County that included every corner of the hospital, from
the morgue to the staff dining room.

In each hospital, I had persons who might be considered
"informants," namely those with whom I had developed
friendships and who, in conversation, supplied me with much
information about their circumstances of work, technical
matters, feelings about the institution, the practices of others
and information about happenings which took place when I
was not present. In nearly every setting, I managed to be-
friend some worker and gain access to some hidden features.

Occasionally I was treated with, what was from my standpoint, a bit too much enthusiasm. At County, several interns,
fresh out of medical school and anxious to demonstrate their
grasp on the world of biophysical fact, gave me long lectures on the structure of the human organism, complete with
live bedside demonstrations. Some of them even insisted
that I "feel this," "press here," "put your hand over there."

At times I was enlisted to assist in a particular procedure
by passing an instrument, helping prop up a patient, tighten
a tourniquet and the like, all of which I did to make myself

as much a part of the scene as possible. By helping the
morgue attendant transfer a deceased patient from the bed
to the stretcher, I made him feel as though his actions were
not being so distantly observed as when I stood in the background and silently watched him at work. (It is interesting
that young interns particularly, regarded my interest as essentially in technical aspects of "dying." For the most part,
I seem to have been regarded as some sort of a medical in-
vestigator.)

THE CENTRAL PROBLEM

Early in the course of my fieldwork I became aware that
staff members' definitions of "dying" and "dead" were not
entirely consonant with my own. In my initial forays onto
the hospital wards, I found myself feeling that everyone
seemed to be dying, particularly so on the acute medical
wards at County, where most of the persons were very old
and very ill. As I made my "rounds" from ward to ward
each morning, I found that nurses directed my attention to
particular cases. My role was defined as that of one concerned with "death," and staff members took it upon themselves to point the proper way. It reached a point, in fact,
where inquiries were not necessary on my part, but where
simply upon my arrival on the ward, announcements of the
status of patients' conditions with respect to their likely
demise greeted me. This became an object of some joking,
unpleasant to me, as staff members referred to me as the
"death man," and in some cases "the ghoul."

On each ward, the head nurse or assistant head nurse
could usually be relied upon to furnish accurate information
about death likelihoods. I discovered that many of the patients who, on the basis of my assessments of their appearance, age and illness, I would have expected to be considered
as "dying," were not so regarded by nursing and medical

personnel. On one of my early days at County, a head nurse, seeing me enter the room of an elderly lady who was suffering from advanced carcinoma, said, "Oh, she's O.K., she won't go this time," and I was directed to another woman who was described as "just about to go." Regularly, when I made inquiries about "who is dying," I was directed to cases where death was immediately expected, within the next few hours or, at most, days. When upon arriving at a new ward for the first time I was introduced to a physician in charge as one "interested in studying death," I was immediately given a rundown which consisted of a census of likely candidates.

I became impressed by the fact that for members of the staff, "dying," rather than being generally usable as a description of persons who were on a steady downward course, was reserved for those who were likely to die during their current hospital admission. While I had naïvely entered the setting thinking of "dying" as a notion used for persons who had, say, cancer, I came to see that for members of the staff, the usage is restricted to that condition which is taken to warrant a very special set of treatments. I soon realized that what was needed to place the event within an organizational framework, was what might be called a "procedural definition" of "dying," one which consulted those practices which "dying" could be said to consist of for members of the staff.

By examining the practices in the care of patients, I have been able to give at least a first approximation to the notions of "dying" and "death" as social facts, matters whose significance is largely established by the practical, organizational concerns of those who daily deal with such occurrences. Rather than settle upon some arbitrary definition of "dying patients" and "dead patients," and proceed from there, I found it more suitable to make the definitional issue a matter of my research. In some senses then, Chapters III and IV particularly, can be read as a "guide to finding 'dying' patients." Unless discussed in terms of the practical work concerns of hospital personnel and the requirements of the hospital social organization the notions "dying" and "death" can have a very unclear meaning.

In the course of my research, a series of special topics came to interest me and I have tried to incorporate discussions of them within the general theme of the study. In Chapter III, I have included a discussion of some of the special problems of the "morgue attendant," that person in the hospital most continuously involved in the grossest aspects of body work. Some of the problems he experienced in his work are shared by those members of the society who, by virtue of the kind of work they do, find themselves continually seen as "on the job." With a very limited degree of flexibility, what they are up to is always available for others to see, and as a consequence their work life is characterized by special types of pressure.

While investigating deaths in various places throughout the hospital, I was intrigued by the special problems which plague hospital staff and administrators and constitute a recurrent topic of many theological considerations, namely those surrounding the treatment of premature and younger fetus deaths. While much more can be said about this area, its legal, social and administrative aspects (and while there is a particularly interesting investigation yet to be made into the structure of "bereavement" in the case of such "deaths"), I have restricted my attention here to matters which are in accord with the general theme of the study; namely the impact of the hospital social organization upon the care and treatment of the dying and the dead.

Within the general framework of the study's theme, I have sought to be as descriptive as possible, keeping uppermost the concern to provide a documentation of facts of hospital life and death hitherto either unseen or unnoticed by outsiders. I feel it a shortcoming of research on hospitals that, with very few exceptions, no detailed accounting of patient care practices is available. Whatever work is available on "death in the hospital" is generally based on field interviews, rather removed from actual instances of dying, which rely heavily on the use of informants who retrospectively report their attitudes and happenings at the time of the death. Whatever contribution this study might make as an addition to that research will hopefully derive from the fact that the information it contains was gained firsthand.

II

The Setting of the County Hospital

County Hospital is a 440-bed, acute treatment, general hospital for the indigent. Theoretically, County "provides medical care, through its regular inpatient and outpatient divisions, for all indigent residents of the county." The fact that it is an indigent or charity hospital can be misleading, however, in that, as in most such institutions, the care it provides is rarely free.[1] While only a small percentage of the patients, less than twenty-five percent, ever pay their bills, rather consistent efforts are made, with the support of local law enforcement agencies, to collect as much as is feasible of the total assessed amount.

County is located in a city with a rather sizeable and somewhat transient cohort of recently migrant Southern Negroes who reside in the city's extensive slum district. The community has something of a reputation for being a center for migrating Negroes, considered by some as the "Chicago of the postwar era." It is the slum district's inhabitants who constitute the core of County's patient population.

The hospital is in a transitional neighborhood of old, deteriorating wooden homes, occasionally interspersed with

newer duplex-type apartment buildings. The physical plant
is something of an eyesore, which might be architecturally
described as early twentieth-century "American Gothic." A
grayish-brown building, it sprawls rather haphazardly along
the edge of a hillside, and is bounded by large walls and
moderately busy streets. To reach the main entrance from
the street, one has to climb what appears as an infinite number of steps, up a rather steep incline.

The building's hallways are dingy, poorly lit and badly
ventilated. There are no visitors' eating facilities, with the
"exception" of a few old vending machines, which are typically out of order. The gift shop which is commonly found
in middle-class hospitals is, congruent with other facts about
County, absent. A newcomer quickly detects a range of
rather obnoxious odors, more poignant than usually encountered in the public parts of most hospitals, which add to the
generally depressing mood of the setting. The only relatively
bright spots in the building are those places which are set
aside for use by the medical and nursing staff, such as
lounges, cafeterias, offices and the new clinic building, ad-
joined to the main plant by a long and airy corridor. There
are gardens surrounding the building, all of which are carefully planted and groomed and seldom used. In its overall
physical structure, the hospital appears considerably di-
lapidated.[2]

The main plant consists of a long, narrow building, four
floors high. On each floor there is a long, wide corridor,
from which branch four wings. The wings on each floor are
referred to as "wards," each designated for a different
medical or surgical service. The hospital has the usual range
of divisions: medicine, surgery, obstetrics, pediatrics, ortho-
pedics etc., but not the more specialized services (neurology,
cancer ward, opthamology, audiology, cardiology) which
are often found in research-oriented and wealthier institutions. On the medical wards, diseases from diabetes to can-

cer to glaucoma to syphilis will be found, and patients with
quite dissimilar medical problems often are assigned to the
same rooms.

Although called "wards," the wings differ from what
typically goes by this term. Each "ward" or wing is an arm
of the central corridor and is unofficially divided into two
sections, that half closest to the central corridor (which
is perpendicular to the ward corridor) being reserved for
the more seriously ill patients, the outside half, farthest
from the main corridor, for the ambulatory and semi-am-
bulatory patients. A nurses' station constitutes the division
between the two sections, and adjacent to it are a supply
room, sterilization room, examination room and small laboratory. The larger "ward" rooms, six and eight beds each,
are in the "ambulatory section," and the private, semiprivate, and four-bed rooms in the "critically ill" half. Each of
the sixteen hospital wards is physically identical, though located on different floors as independent arms off the main
corridor. At the main corridor end of the ward is an old
elevator, officially designated for hospital staff only, though
not always so exclusively used. There are large elevators in
the central part of the hospital, where the main corridor
joins the corridor to the clinic building, and where administrative offices, operating rooms and cafeterias for employees
are located. These elevators are marked for visitors' use.
Unlike hospitals such as Cohen, all elevators in County are
visible to visitors so that what is being transported from
floor to floor, including dead bodies, is potentially seen by
properly situated onlookers. The overall physical layout is
not generally structured to provide clearly public and clearly
nonpublic places, with the exception of the operating room
area, the maternity ward and the premature nursery.

Each ward corridor is some seventy-five feet in length and
ten feet wide, the main corridor which runs the entire length
of the hospital being considerably wider. The private and

semiprivate rooms are quite tiny by most contemporary hospital standards. Aside from the bed, there is a single wooden
chair and small, wooden nightstand per patient; the over-
head light supplies the only illumination as there are no individual bed lights. The private room is about ten by eight
feet in dimension, the semiprivate room about ten by fifteen.
While apparently clean and freshly painted, the ward and
rooms are very drab and poorly ventilated. There are no
visitors' waiting rooms on the ward itself; the only place a
visitor can await the beginning of visiting hours is in the
general hospital lobby at the front of the building which,
with its long benches, resembles a train station. If, during a
visit with a patient, a relative is asked to leave the room, he
must stand in the ward corridor. The doors to individual
rooms are rarely kept closed, so that a visitor can witness
nearly everything that goes on in neighboring rooms. While
curtains surround each bed in the multi-bed rooms, they are
not always drawn at appropriate points. During visiting
hours, as one walks down the hall to a patient's room, he is
quite likely to see several patients' bodies exposed as bed-
clothes are being changed or examinations conducted. With
the exception of certain occasions, the use of curtains to
screen off a bed is made as a gesture and not seriously, so
that there is nearly always a degree of openness of the
screen, with consequent visibility for an onlooker. I found
this to be true myself as I walked down ward corridors
through areas where it was proper for visitors to be, though
it is not altogether clear that among County's patient and
relative population such visibility would be a noticeable matter. It may be a feature which is striking only to middle-class
eyes.

The general extent of "security measures" at County is
noticeably less than at Cohen. While there are considerably
fewer visitors around the hospital than is the case at Cohen,
restrictions on their freedom of movement are not very

great. On the obstetrics ward at Cohen, when the "babies
are out" (when infants are being taken to their mothers
for feeding), a nurse stands guard at the elevator to prohibit the entry of unauthorized people, which includes, in
addition to visitors, all hospital personnel who do not have
rightful business on the maternity floor. This restriction also
applies to physicians who have no patients on the floor. At
County Hospital, the infant nursery is on a different floor
than the maternity patients' beds, and babies are brought
up in the elevator, carried by student nurses, when feeding
time approaches. While some effort is made to insure that
the elevator will be unoccupied, on numerous occasions I observed persons other than nurses riding along, such as jani-
tors, visitors, physicians. When such a practice was related
to OB personnel at Cohen, they expressed shock at the implied lack of concern with asepsis. When mothers nurse their
infants at Cohen, curtains are drawn between their beds to
afford privacy and presumably limit the possibilities of germ
spread from one mother to another's child.

At County, the method of child-feeding typifies certain
general features of the atmosphere of the hospital. At appointed hours during the day, the student nurses depart, *en
masse,* from where they are working and go to "pick up
babies" from the nursery. At a coordinated moment, an OB
nurse rings a loud buzzer which signifies to recuperating
mothers that it is "feeding time," whereupon the mothers,
in their characteristic postdelivery shuffle, form a rough line
in the corridor and painfully meander down the hall to a
large "feeding room." In this feeding room are a dozen or
so old rocking chairs, set in a cozy circle, where the mothers
sit, prepare their breasts for feeding and await the arrival
of the nurses' brigade. Those mothers who are not breast-
feeding their babies (and the proportion of them is very low
at County and quite high at Cohen) are provided with prepared formula bottles. Apparently, public feeding would be

an intolerable practice at modest, middle-class institutions where, at least as in the case of Cohen, privacy at feeding time is cherished and infringements upon it negatively sanctioned. The fact that I was freely permitted to observe the mass-feeding practice at County, yet treated much as a visitor at feeding time at Cohen, is partially indicative of the general ideological difference between the two hospitals.

Throughout County, many aspects of medical care are oriented on a mass basis. Most X-ray examinations are done in the morning hours, when the doctors' orders from the previous day are consulted to prepare those patients for X-ray whose examination has been requested. While at Cohen patients are individually taken to X-ray, at County several are taken at one time, by a group of attendants. There is a morning line-up of stretchers and after all patients scheduled for radiological examinations have been assembled, a group of attendants march them off together. It is not improper to employ a rationale which says: "There's no use having an attendant removed from other work just to take one patient over to X-ray." Similarly, laboratory tests are ordered in batches, rather than on a one-by-one basis. If a physician has to do a pelvic examination he will go through the charts to see if any other such examinations on other patients are needed, and if so, try to do them all at the same time, one right after the other. For a certain range of tasks, like taking blood pressures, temperatures and pulse readings, at all hospitals there is a tendency to schedule such activities within a strict clock routine, and do them for all patients at every point on the clock schedule. At County, one finds similar scheduling for those activities, which, at Cohen, would not be so scheduled.

At Cohen, nearly every ward has its own EKG (electrocardiogram) machine. At County, there is a limited number of such machines and the administration of EKG examinations is done on a routinized basis. A woman technician

spends her entire day wheeling an EKG machine about systematically through the hospital's wards, checks the charts
on each ward, and does EKG's on all patients for whom
they are ordered. If a physician orders an EKG, he must
wait for the technician's round to bring her to his ward. In
Emergency Ward routine, EKG machines are available for
case-by-case use, but elsewhere in the hospital, one places an
order and awaits the arrival of the machine. In many respects, the County patient's care is at the mercy of the
scheduled character of medical care activities, whereas at
Cohen such schedules are so frequently violated by physicians' requests to "have it done now," that the request rather
than the schedule is the principled basis for administering
treatments.

The feasibility of routinizing mass treatment is enhanced
by the fact that at County, there are no private patients.
Physicians treat a group; the central principle for the allocation of work being geographical, the physician mans a
ward and treats its patients. This fact has several rather
important consequences which shall be discussed shortly and
referred to repeatedly in the course of later chapters. First,
a few words about the character of the medical staff.

THE STAFF

The chief sense in which County is a "county hospital"
seems to lie in the fact that no private patients are treated
there. While a given patient might have a "private physician," should that person be admitted to County, his own
physician can no longer treat him. Referrals to County by
private physicians are rather infrequently made, and typically only under the circumstance that hospital care is considered quite essential and the patient has no funds. All patients are the patients of the hospital's employed intern and
resident physicians. In hospital terminology, County's staff

is strictly a "house staff." These doctors are under the general supervision of a county-salaried medical director, the chief administrator of the hospital, and assume full responsibility for the admission, treatment and discharge of all patients.

The medical staff consists of approximately forty-five interns, thirty residents, and a dozen part-time division directors. The actual number of physicians in the house at any one time, and from year to year, varies slightly depending upon the hospital's success in recruiting new interns and residents. In recent years the number of applications for internships and residencies has been roughly equal to the number of positions available, so that nearly all applicants are accepted.

Private physicians are appointed, with token salaries, to posts as the "directors" of various hospital services. Their central responsibility is to make "grand medical rounds" each week with the permanent house staff. They do not treat patients directly, nor may they admit their own patients to the hospital. They are essentially consultants, with a very limited voice in matters of general hospital and medical policy. Unlike the "private physician" at Cohen Hospital, they have no final word in the treatment decisions on any given case. This authority rests with the chief resident of the service.

In addition to these nominal directors of services, a group of private physicians rotates through the hospital, one month each per year, offering free consultative "charity" service. During his month of service, a private physician comes to the hospital two mornings a week and makes daily rounds with the house staff, providing general consultative advice. He has no authority in planning treatment, that authority residing solely with the house staff within which the intern is answerable to the resident, the resident to the chief resident and the chief resident to the medical director. At

Cohen the visiting man is a key figure and not really a visitor insofar as nearly all of his hospitalized patients are at Cohen Hospital, and he often spends a considerable part of his day in the hospital. At County, the visiting man is a true visitor, with very limited say-so. In his presence, he is accorded polite deference; behind his back he is regarded as something of an intruder. Interactions between house staff and visiting men have the character of "going through the motions," seemingly recognized mutually by both parties. At Cohen Hospital, a resident is often obliged to "have a consult" on a "service" patient (a patient who has no private physician), meaning that he is obliged to seek the advice of a visiting man before instituting treatment, and the decision of the visiting man is binding. At County, the only people with such authority are the residents. A resident at Cohen who was having difficulty locating his "consult" and was thereby held up in his treatment of a patient (and made to stay on after his shift was over) complained, "Oh, for the good old days of the county hospital where we didn't have to go through this nonsense."

The resident and intern physicians at County are drawn primarily from the state university medical schools, and among these, the average quality schools. Of the forty-five interns, some thirty came from schools such as the University of Iowa, Nebraska, Oregon, Washington, California, Utah, North Carolina, Tennessee, Wisconsin, Michigan, Alabama, Indiana, Georgia. A few came from smaller colleges of lesser repute; none were graduates of the bigger and better known medical schools such as Chicago, Harvard, Yale, Stanford, Kansas, Washington University, Johns Hopkins, Columbia. From what can be gathered from conversation with hospital administrators, most of the interns were in the second quarter of their graduating classes, between the fiftieth and seventy-fifth percentiles. County seems to get the better than average but not top-notch students from the fairly respectable state university medical schools. The relatively high proportion of interns who stay on at County seems partially explainable by the difficulty County interns have in getting residency posts in other institutions, for many of them try unsuccessfully to move elsewhere.[3]

As a hospital with no visiting staff, there is a general upgrading of the level of responsibility given to intern and resident physicians. In the private hospital, an internship is very often rightly regarded as involving quite menial, nonresponsible work. At County, however, interns are given responsibility to engage in medical activities which, in private hospitals, would be allowable only for residents. Likewise, residents are granted much less freedom of movement and responsibility for independent decision making in the private hospital than at County. All through the staff hierarchy at County, we find a generally greater amount of responsibility independently assumed by personnel than would be assumed by similarly stationed personnel in the private hospital setting. Several examples can be given: At County, nearly all babies are delivered by interns and residents, and nurses assist by giving anesthesia, when necessary. At Cohen Hospital, all deliveries are performed by private physicians or residents, and the latter only on "service patients." At County, first year residents often assume complete charge of relatively routine but major surgical procedures such as appendectomies. The intern assists with suturing. At Cohen Hospital, first year residents never make incisions and interns are never allowed to do suturing, these tasks being allotted to the advanced resident and junior resident respectively. At Cohen, the student nurse is generally not allowed to start an intravenous injection; at County, an intern would consider it beneath him to be asked to start an IV, and oftentimes so would a nurse, who would call upon a student.

Some IV solutions are administered through what is known as a "cutdown." Here, in part because of the potency

of the solution being administered and the concern to not
have that solution invade surrounding tissue, a small incision is made, typically in the leg, a vein is located, severed
and affixed to the IV needle to permit sure entry of the medicine directly into the blood stream. At County, interns regularly do cutdowns, in fact residents have been known to
call upon interns to do them. At Cohen, interns are not permitted to perform the procedure, but only to assist the resident, who does the major work.

Generally, the "absence" of the private physician lowers
the upper level of authority and upgrades the domains of
responsibility at all staff levels. A newcomer to County gets
the initial and perhaps lasting impression of a hospital "run
by boys." It is, at least at first, quite incongruous, perhaps
only to the middle-class observer, to see quite young men
delivering babies, doing surgery, and the like. The "traditional" image of the physician, whose countenance and bedside manner convey experience, is as markedly absent at
County as it is present at Cohen. The average age of the
County physician is twenty-eight, that of the Cohen doctor
in the forties.

The "absence" of the practicing, experienced specialist
that one generally finds in the key authority position in many
university affiliated hospitals and private institutions provides a special character both to the kind of "learning" one
does at County, and to the kind of medicine and surgery
practiced there. At County, residents and interns learn almost exclusively from each other. There is no visible outside
source of knowledge and experience except that of the textbook and the extremely nonsystematic instruction provided,
on a very occasional basis, by the "visiting man." The intern
learns from the resident and the resident from other residents.

This lack of daily contact with the outside world of medical practice provides for a general technological stagnation.

Many procedures, which have long since been abandoned in favor of more modern practices at other hospitals, are still much in vogue at County. The relatively low budget for the purchase of new equipment is only a partial explanation; the general lack of contact with long-term experience seems quite important. Many County physicians are aware of the "cultural lag" and recognize that the sheer fact that its young men have been exposed to modern medical school training is not sufficient a basis for innovation and change. Keeping pace with current developments best occurs once one has left an internship and residency and begins to actively practice his specialty in interaction with colleagues.

The physician at County does a "tour of duty." The clock and calendar govern the way the intern's time is allocated, and not the particular patients who happen to be his charge for the day. Once he is "off duty," he relegates his care of the patient to his colleague, and the latter does not feel obligated to consult the former to get clearance for instituting a treatment, nor does the former feel particularly obligated to retain any control over the patient's care. While a wide degree of latitude is given younger personnel regarding their rights to perform complicated procedures, perhaps "responsibility" is not an appropriate term, for the County physician's obligations are not as closely controlled as the Cohen physician's, who is answerable at many points to a formidable collection of superiors. It is important to note that one of the main differences between being a physician at County and at Cohen derives from the fact that given the lack of a historical development and involvement with relatives and patients, County doctors can interchange with one another in the performance of a wide range of tasks. Once a history between physician and relative and physician and patient has become well-established, and a traditional "doctor-patient-relative" contractual understanding reached, a certain segment of the doctor's tasks can no longer be relegated or delegated to other doctors to perform. At County Hospital, the delegation of tasks is quite common, and extends to tasks which, at Cohen, would not be properly delegateable, including talking to the family about the patient's condition and doing surgery. It can be parenthetically noted that presumably one of the key worries some persons have about "socialized" medicine derives from the possibility that such arrangements will mitigate the development of a continuous doctor-patient relationship and thus allow for relatively uncontrolled interchangeability of physicians. At the same time, this constitutes one of the central freedoms of such arrangements for physicians, although one which is apparently not of great enough import to stand as a good reason for such arrangements.[4]

The County physician consequently finds that his attachments are a thing of the moment, and that at any point in the day, by virtue of the fact that he is an employee of the hospital and not a "visitor with a patient," he may find himself suddenly thrust into the midst of a case, the beginning and end of which he will never have a part in. The ward of the hospital is, from the County intern or resident's perspective, an environment of medical events, not persons, to a somewhat greater extent than seems to be the case with the physician in the "private hospital." A commonly expressed feeling among County physicians is that the private practice at least offers the advantage of being able to select one's patients, yet at the same time, the interchangeability of physicians is valued by County physicians because it allows getting uninvolved with those patients who are regarded as less than desirable social types.

The absence of the visiting physician who spends much of his career practicing medicine in the same hospital, gives County Hospital a rather special organizational quality. Every year there is a complete turnover of the intern population, and every fourth year, of the entire medical staff.

County's staff members (partially perhaps as a consequence
of this turnover) have a limited degree of interest in the
institution itself, regarding it as a temporary field setting
rather than an organization whose ideology, development
and reputation, affects and reflects their own. There is a
characteristic attitude of indifference toward the setting.
Doctors frequently talk negatively of the facilities and the
patient population, not so much as to indicate a desire for
change and improvement, as to maintain a social distance
from implicit identification with "this kind of medicine" and
"this kind of patient." The key source of continuity during
this change of staff is the nursing division, whose personnel
constitute the only permanent people on the scene. While at
Cohen, the new medical staff member learns local culture
from upper echelon medical people, this is only partially so
at County where the nurse is regarded as a much more important person, one whom the physician can and must consult on a wide variety of organizational matters.

There is a characteristic period of relative chaos and conflict at the beginning of the new year when the incoming
crop of interns arrives. Freed from the disciplines of medical school life, the new doctor now is one who gives orders
and mobilizes the resources of the hospital in the care of his
patient. A period of several weeks is considered necessary
for the intern to learn to respect the wisdom of the nurse,
on whom he must rely to learn almost everything he has to
know to get along in County. He must learn to respect the
fact that the hospital, despite the near absence of super-
visory physicians, nonetheless has an order which was con-
structed without regard for him, in which he must "make
it." Giving orders characteristically involves tension. Young
doctors abruptly order old time nurses about, and nurses
answer, "Get it yourself," disillusioning physicians about
the scope of respect they will legitimately receive.

LIFE AND DEATH MEDICINE

The overall character of medical and surgical care at County is rather decidedly directed toward the treatment of advanced illness rather than oriented in preventive directions. The intern and resident at County treat many more very sick patients than Cohen physicians do. It is common to find patients admitted to Cohen Hospital for "observation" or for general "checkups." At County, while diagnostic problems are the order of the day, diagnostic attention is chiefly directed toward treatment of the seriously ill and not toward early detection of possible serious illness. Any morning in the X-ray department at Cohen will find several patients, in good physical condition, awaiting routine chest and abdominal examinations as part of the yearly medical exam. The X-ray department at County always finds many patients lying on stretchers, escorted by attendants, in rather sickly condition. There is no "elective surgery" at County; the surgery which is done there is done because the house staff considers it necessary in the course of the current treatment of the patient. Various types of surgery are far more frequent at Cohen Hospital than at County, for example: herniorrhaphies (hernia repair surgery), hysterectomies, cholecystectomies (gall bladder removal), mastectomies (breast removals). Hernia and hysterectomy surgery are generally done under the circumstance of physical discomfort and not for specific illness treatment. Hernia complaints typically involve lower abdominal pain, with no interference with physical functioning, and this "corrective surgery" is often close to "cosmetic surgery" in its general import. At Cohen, many herniorrhaphies are done as "corrective repair surgery;" at County such procedures are typically performed only when some essential functioning has been impaired and the hernia repair is essential to life. Likewise, hysterectomies are very often electively contracted to relieve physical discomfort rather than to treat dangerous functional disorders. At Cohen, this surgery is quite frequently done (and among its population of middle-class women, often fashionable), whereas at County, gynecological surgery is usually done only when organ functioning is impaired, when severe infection occurs from an ovarian cyst, or when cancerous tissue is located. Procedures like gallbladder and breast removals are typically instigated upon early detection of the need for them. Many gallbladder removals are "unnecessary," done to prevent the possibility of a serious emergency condition, the likelihood of which is not always considered sufficiently high as to warrant the procedure. Breast removals are done at the earliest detection of cancerous tissue. Once a breast cancer becomes extensive and metastasizes, removal of the breast is no longer a preventive measure and may become, medically speaking, useless. Among Cohen's middle-class patient population, early detection of breast tumors is much more likely than among County's base patient population, and mastectomies are done many times a week.

Personnel regard the general atmosphere at County as somewhat depressing. The tenor of activity is relatively morbid; the practice of medicine and surgery there is predominantly massive in its scope. A great deal of activity takes place in the Emergency Unit, where most "suspects" are treated and victims of violence patched up. Staff have claimed that local police officials favor the use of Emergency Unit facilities as relatively safe places to coerce and beat criminal suspects.

There is a small office in the ward which is directly in the view of the public waiting room, designated as a "Press Room," to which suspects are taken by police when blood tests for alcoholism are given. The staff of the ward is responsible for giving such tests on a policeman's request. On several occasions police have been known to bring suspects there and, as it appears from the noise that issues from that room, beat them. While the police are apparently not troubled about what people overhear while they are in the room, on numerous occasions rather harsh words have been exchanged between them and nursing and medical personnel who maintain that the room is being improperly used. During a period of nine months several formal protests were made by the hospital to the police department, but at the end of that period, such "beatings" were still being heard, particularly on Saturday nights. A nurse commented: "The cops wouldn't dare do that on the streets where they could be seen, so they come in here where they think no one will say anything."

The Emergency Ward has two holding cells, much like prison cells, where suspects receiving medical treatment and requiring overnight care are kept during their transit from the street to prison. This facility is a distinctive mark of the County Hospital, along with the general appearance of large numbers of policemen in the Emergency Ward on busy weekend evenings. When police officers accompany prisoners to the hospital for treatment, they have the legal right and duty to stay with their prisoners while they are seen by a physician.

It is common in the Emergency Ward to find policemen restraining alcoholic and epileptic prisoners while they are being examined and treated by the attending physician. On such occasions, nurses, who would normally assist in treating such patients, are relieved by policemen, who are often less than totally mindful of the physiological effects of the way in which they employ restraints. On several occasions, a particular surgical resident refused to examine "police patients" because of the ways they were handled by police. Generally, however, nurses leave the room and doctors quietly treat the policeman's charge. Some physicians often page for a policeman to come into a treatment room and aid in subduing an alcoholic patient who is "causing trouble." On several nights there have been fist fights in the treatment rooms; in one case a policeman hit a man who was cursing him while being bandaged for facial lacerations.

On the medical wards at County, one finds a high frequency of alcoholism-related diseases; liver, spleen and kidney disorders, and many diabetic patients whose conditions are complicated by alcoholism. There are so many jaundiced patients that a nurse who came to work at County after having been employed at a private hospital for many years commented, "I've never seen so many yellow people in my whole life." The number of venereal disease patients at County is much greater than at Cohen. On the surgical floors, one finds a substantial number of patients being treated for gunshot wounds, stab wounds, fractures, concussions, and other traumatic injuries.

In this chapter I have tried to present a very general background picture of some prominent aspects of County Hospital. A much more detailed discussion of a variety of organizational features, particularly those relating to death, will be presented in the course of my discussion of specific topics in the following chapters. Rather than ask the reader to keep these features in mind, they shall be introduced at appropriate points in the course of the book.

III

Who Died?

On the average, three persons die in County Hospital each day, with variations as great as from none at all to fifteen in a given twenty-four hour period.

The deaths are distributed throughout the hospital, with the greatest frequency occurring on the medical and surgical floors. The personnel on these wards therefore encounter deaths rather frequently. Within the course of a first week on the job, a new orderly or attendant will have assisted in removing several patients' bodies from the ward, the new intern will have pronounced several patients dead and the new nurses' aide will have "wrapped" several bodies.

These wards, unlike others in the hospital, are specially oriented to the occurrence of deaths as routine, daily events. This orientation is clearly seen with respect to certain practices related to the processing of a dead body. When a patient dies, his body must be properly prepared before it is removed from the ward. This preparation, which shall be discussed in greater detail in the next chapter, requires, among other things, wrapping the body in a "morgue sheet." The central supply office has such sheets, and assembles them into "morgue bundles." In addition to the heavy muslin sheet used to wrap the body, these include identification tags to be affixed to the corpse, special cotton-covered strings for tying the hands and feet together and a pair of precut gauze pads to be placed over the deceased's eyes. The practice employed by all wards, except the medical and surgical ones, is to telephone the central supply office when a death occurs, and request that a "morgue bundle" be sent up to the ward. On the medical and surgical wards, however, a large storage of these bundles, usually exceeding several dozen, is kept in the ward supply closet, along with other equipment.

The orientation to death as a continual and routine possibility can also be seen in the fact that on the medical and surgical wards there is always a "morgue tray" kept on hand. When the morgue attendant arrives on most hospital wards to "pick up a body" for removal to the morgue, he brings a tray with him. The morgue tray, unlike a regular "guerney," is unpadded and has a special top grooved to fit the morgue refrigerator compartments when lifted off its wheels. The medical and surgical wards, however, retain their own morgue stretchers or trays which they use if a patient dies after 3:30 P.M., and the morgue is closed for official business. When a death occurs in the late afternoon or evening, ward personnel must remove the body to the morgue themselves. To avoid a long walk to the basement morgue to secure a special tray, or the necessity of having to take the body downstairs on a regular stretcher and then transfer it onto a second fitted tray (a particularly disliked task, especially if one is alone and has to struggle to keep the body from falling off onto the floor), these wards keep such trays on hand.

Autopsy permits, the legal form which surviving relatives must sign before a postmortem examination may be properly performed, are kept at the nurses' stations throughout the hospital. An interesting difference between the medical and surgical and other service wards relates to the way such forms are assembled: Usually there is, in a desk drawer at the nurses' station, a series of folders containing the various forms used for varieties of administrative matters. These include "consent to perform surgery," "admission," "discharge," "narcotics order," "release of personal belongings," and a host of others. Forms which must be filled out when a death occurs include the "death certificate," the "autopsy permit," the "release of personal belongings" form and the "provisional death certificate," a working sheet on which a tentative diagnosis of the "cause of death" is listed before the formal death certificate is completed. On the medical and surgical floors, these "death forms" are stapled together into one unit. It is not uncommon to find the desk clerk, when doing her daily inventories and straightening about during slack hours, collating these forms and assembling them into "death packages." This is not done elsewhere in the hospital, the forms being assembled only if and when a death occurs. Deaths do not occur on the medical and surgical wards with such frequency that the assembling of such forms in advance would seem to be technically required for instant use. The fact that this is done is an indication of the way the occurrence of deaths is regarded, namely as a recurrent, daily happening of ward life.

COUNTING DEATHS

On high-death wards staff members frequently ask, upon coming to work "How many today?" Deaths are counted, not with any special extraordinary interest, but along with such matters as the number of new admissions, the number of occupied beds and the number of discharges. The opening of a "report" session (that ritual wherein the new shift of nurses receives its briefing from the outgoing shift) typically includes the following prefatory tallies: "We have a full house, Mrs. W. was discharged this A.M., a patient is expected in tonight who'll go to room seven, Mrs. P. died this morning;" or "No deaths, three empty beds, quiet night ahead." [1] Then the details of patients' progress and treatment schedules are reviewed. Nurses on these wards leave work at the close of their shift expecting that some patients they have cared for during the day will die during their absence, and frequently they make inquiries upon arriving at work to confirm their expectations. Some nurses characteristically look into doorways of those rooms wherein "dying" patients had been known to be the day before, to see if they are still alive and present. The following recorded sequents of conversation between nurses at shift change indicate the manner in which such inventories are made and convey a sense of the general import of noticing the occurrence of a death:

A: Hi Sue, bet you're ready to go home.
B: You ain't just kiddin'. It's been a busy one!
A: What's new?
B: Nothin' much. Oh yes, Mrs. Wilkins, poor soul, died this morning, just after I got here.
A: I didn't think she'd make it that long. Do we have a full house?
B: Just about. Number two's empty, and seven I think.

A: Mrs. Jones die?
B: I think so, let me see (looks at charts). Guess so. (Turns to other nurse) Did Mrs. Jones die today?
C: She was dead before I got into work this morning, must have died during the night.
A: Poor dear. I hardly knew her but she looked like a nice old lady.

A: You look tired.
B: I am. Lucky you, it's all yours.
A: I hope it's a quiet night. I'm not too enthusiastic.
B: They all died during the day today, lucky us, so you'll probably have it nice and easy.

A: So I saw. Looks like three, four and five are empty.

B: Can you believe it, we had five deaths in the last twelve hours.

A: How lovely.

B: Well, see you tomorrow night. Have fun.

The announcement of a death from one shift member to another can and does occur in the course of an ordinary conversation, and on these wards, where deaths are not so much announced as they are mentioned, their mention does not noticeably inhibit ordinary conversation.

However, when a death occurs in an unexpected place or under rather unusual circumstances, news spreads quickly and the character of conversation about death is much more dramatic. On one occasion a diabetic woman died in childbirth (a relatively infrequent happening) and by the time a nurse arrived on the OB ward for the evening shift, she had already heard of the morning's death. She was greeted by a daytime nurse as she approached the station with "Have you heard?" She answered, "Yes, Mrs. B. stopped me in the hall downstairs and told me," whereupon a conversation was entered about "what happened" with detailed reporting of "what she said," "why did they do that?," "then what did he do," far exceeding that which normally attends the discussion of deaths on the medical and surgical wards.

New student nurses and, apparently, young medical students make it a habit of counting such events as deaths, and locate their own growing experience by reference to "how many times" such and such has been encountered, witnessed and done. One apparent mark of sophistication among one's peers is reached at that point when some occurrences are no longer counted, when "I've lost count" is properly given as an answer.

An informant student nurse reported that young students count, and report their counts in informal conversation, nearly everything from the number of injections they have given and enemas administered to the number of operations they have witnessed, autopsies attended, deaths of their patients and other patients' "dead bodies seen." The commonplace events, though, quickly lose their countability. In fact, the "count" seems to end once the first occasion is superceded by a second. The girl who would report that she had administered her second or third injection would be regarded by her peers, my informant reports, as one who was too taken by the trivial tasks of nursing.[2]

In referring to the fact that specific counts of frequent occurrences have "long since been lost," we often find persons pointing to that feature by announcing some number, or using some quasi-numerical way of talking which conveys "having lost count" in a somewhat more powerful way. Examples are "I've given so many injections in my day . . . ," "In the thousands of operations I have seen . . . ," "I have seen dozens of . . ." These "numerical" ways of describing some state of experience are to be clearly distinguished from those which involve specific reference to an actual number; "I have seen twelve of . . . ," "In the seven cases of . . ." Deaths are specifically counted in this latter sense, so it appears, to about half a dozen. The highest specific count I was able to elicit when asking nurses, "How many have you seen?" was eight. Never did a student report a figure of more than eight, that number being the approximate maximum point at which "losing count" occurs or must be reported as having occurred. To report a number greater than a handful is to appear overly concerned about death, in either a worried, upset, fearful or overfascinated way. With respect to deaths, at least, the student can safely say, "I've seen so many I've lost count," and not be sanctioned for pretentiously suggesting "having been around a lot" should the actual number she has witnessed turn out to be just slightly over a handful.[3]

The classes of initially countable events do, however, tend

to become partitioned into subclasses, the elements of which are themselves counted but no longer are those of the class as a whole. It is relevant and proper, in the sense of being sanctionably useable in conversation and not a mark of over-concern or naïveté, to count the "number of children you have seen die," but not the "number of deaths you have witnessed" if that latter number exceeds a handful. Likewise, the student nurse who "rotates" through the operating room counts the number of operations she witnesses up to a few, and then, the student informant reported, it is regarded as strange for her to continue to count and report counts of events in the class "operations in general." Further counts would then be made, remembered and reported upon within subcategories, like the number of appendectomies, open heart surgeries, gallbladders and the like.

Particularly noteworthy deaths, those about which lively talk spontaneously occurs, are those which take place in settings where deaths are uncommon, those which occur in non-typical fashions, those which result from accidents or diagnostic and treatment errors and those which occur in the very young patient.

Although the nurses of any tenure on the medical and surgical wards cannot begin to recall the "total number of deaths" they have witnessed, they can, with little hesitation, report the number of suicidal patients whose deaths they were involved in or which have occurred on their wards during their periods of employment. In conversation with a medical service nurse it can be learned that she remembers that she has seen "two patients die from barium enema exams." Very infrequently barium enemas produce death when there is a rupture in the intestinal tract and the barium solution escapes into the abdominal cavity; this sort of occurrence, one which can be construed as an error, often becomes a major topic of staff conversation. Nearly everywhere in the hospital, including the pediatrics ward, personnel can report the number of very young children whose deaths they have witnessed or were in any way involved in. One nurse on that service reported that a particular death was her "thirteenth." If one asks OB nurses, however, to recall how many deaths of newborns they have witnessed, they all (with the exception of the very recent newcomer) report they "have no idea." In certain wards, like the OB ward, adult deaths take on a quite different character. A nurse who was commenting on "delivery room nursing" reported that it was the most "rewarding kind of nursing" with the exception that sometimes it can be very "unpleasant." When questioned about its unpleasantness, she alluded to the fact that when a mother dies in childbirth, that can be very upsetting, enough, apparently, to make the scene not altogether a pleasant work environment. This nurse was the head of the delivery room nursing division. On further questioning she reported that "seven years ago was the last time one (death) occurred." That single death retained its character as a relevant fact about the OB setting. A senior operating room nurse, of some thirty years' experience on the division, related, on the occasion of a death which occurred on the operating table, that this was the sixth she had seen in her time. She remembered each vividly, and could describe the circumstances surrounding every one.

Any given death, however, can be a candidate for later comment when, for some reason, a new death suggests a principle of categorization for searching over "past ones." For example, a patient died and his wife fainted on the hall corridor when told of the death. A nurse mentioned that that was the third time she had seen a "relative actually faint" at the news of a death. When a patient died during the course of a routine morning round a doctor recounted that he had "had that happen to him" once before in medical school.

THE VISIBILITY OF DEATH

Secretaries in the front business offices enter and leave the building via the front door and only superficially enter the hospital proper when they take the elevator to the third floor cafeteria. Their only awareness that "people die at County" is in the daily figures they receive from the admission office, upon which they perform numerous accounting operations. As a happening of their job setting, "death" consists for them in figures about unknown persons, with unknown faces, whose bodies, alive or dead, have never been seen. These personnel are known to purposefully restrict their movements in the building to those places devoid of the life and death aspects of hospital work. The layout of the hospital allows and fosters this restriction, for the administrative quarters are nicely separated from the "sick part." The office personnel can work out a career at County, only occasionally ever seeing a patient or smelling those odors associated with the "sick parts" of the building. The fact that it is a hospital at all lies, for them, merely in the fact that the letters they type, reports they construct and superiors they answer to all have something to do with medicine. The only direct reminder they get of the sick work that goes on at County is in the form of an occasional and faint ambulance siren which is heard in the nearby distance, and in the white coats, gowns and dresses which nearly all but themselves wear in the cafeteria.

Only infrequently does news of the circumstances surrounding a death ever reach these personnel. One most striking occasion was when a murder occurred at County. A sheriff's deputy, escorting a prisoner to the Emergency Ward, reportedly "went berserk" and shot a secretary for what was regarded as "no reason whatever." The event was the occasion for considerable conversation, gossip and publicizing. In the Emergency Ward, where personnel routinely

treat victims of gunshot wounds, ordinary activity was temporarily disordered. Doctors and nurses stood about peering
at the dead woman who lay on the office floor. One nurse
was overheard to say to another, "Look at all that blood."
For what was to the administrator of the division an em-
barrassingly long period, no one would approach the body
to see if the woman was dead. Generally, the scene resembled a street accident or murder. This type of "death," not
a hospital event at all, nor a medically relevant occurrence,
but a newsworthy happening, received attention as a full-
blown incident. While a death, it was not a death-in-an-or-
der, generated from an illness or accident which occurred
outside, but from an internal happening. It was not a "hospital death" but simply a death-in-the-hospital, and as such,
did not get treated as do the routine, daily expirations of
patients. The usual "death procedures" which produce the
statistics which the front office girls handle, were absent, so
that it was not, for them, or anyone, a work-relevant event
at all. It is such "deaths" which these personnel might learn
of over and above their occupational involvement in death
statistics. It is these "deaths in the hospital" about which
details of "how it happened," "who discovered the body,"
"how did he die," will get discussed. Others in this class
which occurred during the period of the investigation included the suicidal death of a psychiatric patient who hung
herself in her room, the heart attack death of a hospital
administrator and the accidental death of an X-ray technician who electrocuted himself while working with his machinery. As an environment of such events, the hospital falls
in a class along with other large organizations, perhaps
slightly more susceptible to them by virtue of the frequent
presence of police-escorted patients (and in the murder case,
the presence of police), the existence of a psychiatric service
and the presence of high-voltage equipment.

The deaths of patients are, of course, learned of more

directly by medical and nursing staff. The higher one's position as a nurse or doctor in the nursing and medical hierarchies, however, the less likely one is to directly witness exposed dead bodies, and still less likely is one apt to physically handle corpses. The nursing administrators and higher echelon physicians will generally encounter dead bodies only as they happen to witness them being transported from the ward to the morgue, after these bodies have already been specially wrapped and covered on a stretcher by a sheet. It is the intern and the ward staff nurse who, among these professional classes, actually view the dead in their beds. However, they will not generally handle them, that task being reserved for the nurses' aides and orderlies whose responsibility it is to prepare bodies for transport from the ward.

The deaths other patients may come to know of, and the bodies they may unwittingly view, are those of persons with whom they may have conversed prior to death, heard converse with others, or who stood, vis-à-vis them, as unknown occupants of neighboring beds. On the medical and surgical wards, once a death has been discovered, not always coincident with when it "occurs," the door to the patient's room is usually closed. On occasion a nurse will post a slip of blank white paper on the door, which is understood by staff as a sign that a dead body lies inside. The door is kept closed until the body has been wrapped and removed from the room by the morgue attendant. While relatives are only infrequently present on the wards at County, when they are in the immediate vicinity of the patient's room there is always the likelihood that they will go into the relative's room and, if not already aware of the death, discover him wrapped up tightly in a bundle. There is also the attended likelihood that a relative will enter the wrong room by mistake, and discover a body. On one occasion, a relative, in a pale white state of apparent shock, staggered to the nurses' station to announce what she had seen. A doctor was at the station and very quickly detecting what had occurred by the conversation he overheard, hurriedly offered the account that they had been trying to contact her (the wife) but had not been able to. In an obviously distraught manner he explained that it was standard practice to prepare patients' bodies after death, and that he was extremely sorry she had had to witness her "husband" in that condition.

The likelihood of such discoveries is very low, primarily because relatives are not about enough and because once a body is wrapped, it is usually transported to the morgue without delay. Additional measures are frequently taken such as posting a guard outside the door, or fastening it in such a way that it will appear stuck to someone who happens upon it unaware of its occupant.

When death occurs in a multi-bed room, more serious problems of management are presented. Once the death is discovered, the curtains around the bed are drawn as tightly as possible, but that itself is apparently not sufficient to keep the event invisible to others. Several practices are routinely instituted in such cases.

One general preventive policy is to try to assign a patient whose death is expected to a private room. The warrant for such assignment at County, unlike at the middle-class institution like Cohen, seems almost entirely based on the expectation of likely death. At Cohen, and other such institutions, a private room is chosen by the patient and his relatives for various reasons, among which are the concern for privacy, the concern for the patient's welfare and in some cases, the mark of status which the cost of such a room implies to others. At County, the private room is assigned by staff, and while privacy is a value, it is privacy of the expected death which is often at issue, and what that privacy entails in the precautionary measures which personnel must take in the treatment of the dying and the death.

As deaths are not always discovered by personnel as soon as they occur, it frequently happens that a roommate will notice the death before members of the staff do. On one occasion, a man yelled hysterically for a nurse, crying aloud, "He's dead," repeatedly, until a staff member arrived. On another occasion a man spent several minutes searching the hall to find a nurse to inform her that the person across from him had just died.[4]

One of three procedures is generally followed after the death has been discovered. If the other patient or patients are considered "sensitive" to their surroundings, the deceased patient is placed on a stretcher and removed to another room to be wrapped for discharge to the morgue, or as occurred in several observed instances, the live patient is taken out of the room under the announced auspices of some purported procedure. The latter practice only occurs, it seems, when the room is semiprivate, a two-bed room and only one live patient has to be removed. When the dead patient is removed from the room, some care must be taken to cover the possibility that others might see the patient as he is removed, and there is often an attempt made to make him look alive. On repeated instances, variations on the following example were observed: a nurse came into the room with an aide, and pretended to be talking to the patient. "Let's go to X-ray," she said, whereupon, with the assistance of the aide, the patient was transferred from the bed to a stretcher, her head straightened, mouth closed, and she was quickly and quietly wheeled out of the room, with the nurse using her body as a screen between the deceased's face and her roommate's bed. Usually, such removal can go unnoticed, at least as best as can be discerned from the reactions of other patients. On occasion, however, a live patient makes some skeptical comment about the dead one, who is being passed off as live, like "Didn't he just go to X-ray," at which point personnel attempt to give an answer that will

temporarily satisfy the requirement of getting the body out
without direct confrontation with the live patient with the
fact that it is a "body," yet one which will not be such an
elaborate answer as to appear blatantly false. In response to
the question, which occurred on one occasion, "Didn't he
already go to X-ray?," the aide, who suspected that the live
patient had some suspicions about the liveliness of his roommate, said simply, "Uh huh," and quickly removed the dead
patient. Care must be taken that conversation doesn't sound
too hushed and that, in their handling of the body, the
sounds are not too loud.

Some personnel are not always sufficiently circumspect in
this regard, notable among them being the county coroner,
who arrives to pick up a "coroner's case" (deaths which are
the "result" of accidents, deaths which occur within the first
twenty-four hours of a hospital admittance, so-called "dead
on arrival cases,"), with a partner, and rather loudly transfers the body from its bed to the special steel tray used for
transport to his van. On one occasion in the Emergency
Unit of the hospital, a man was seen to hide himself under
his bedcovers to make the removal of his deceased roommate less obvious than it was made by the coroner's loud
talk and the clamoring of the steel tray as the body was
transferred onto it. He lay trembling for the duration of
the procedure and only with caution and reassurance by a
nurse eventually came out from under the covers.

A common strategy in removing a body from a room
where other patients are potentially witnesses of the removal, is to have one staff member engage the live pa-
tient(s) in conversation, while others remove the dead
roommate. This frequently occurs when deaths take place
in parts of the hospital where, by virtue of their low frequency, personnel are not routinely oriented to the possibility of death and do not have institutionalized ways of an-

ticipating deaths, for example, by assigning "dying" patients
to private rooms.

The most striking instance of a spontaneous undercover
removal of a deceased patient was observed on the pediatrics ward, when a young child unexpectedly died in a large
ward-type room filled with other children. Nurses on that
service, unaccustomed to handling the problems associated
with the transport of bodies, were perhaps better able to
execute an unnoticed removal. Their concern to do so, unlike that of high-death frequency ward personnel, was not
built into some perfunctorily performed and oftentimes
sloppy routine. A nurse picked up a ball and threw it to a
group of children who were playing at the other end of the
room, exclaiming "Let's have a catch." Another nurse assisted in directing their attention away from the deceased
child's bed, while a doctor and an aide drew the drapes
around the bed. A stretcher was brought in and the child
quickly transferred to it, while a lively game of catch engrossed the other children's attentions, including those bed-
ridden ones who could not participate in it. A nurse reported
that in the hours which followed, none of the children
seemed to indicate that they knew what had happened to the
boy at the end of the ward. When one of them asked, the
next morning, "Where's that boy," he seemed satisfied with
an answer that he had been transferred to another ward, an
answer some variant of which staff members regularly use on
the pediatrics ward to explain the absence of a child who has
died. The fact that this death was supervised by many personnel, in part a fact which resulted from the pattern of
supervision on the pediatrics ward and that death is considered a more serious matter there, placed several people in
the position of being able to quickly manage problems of the
body's visibility.

On the medical and surgical wards, the likelihood of discovery by other patients would be greater were it not that

most patients on those wards are relatively more ill and confined to bed, and that assignment to private rooms further minimizes the likelihood of discovery by others.[5] To sustain the pattern of infrequent scrutiny which marks the medical and surgical wards, arrangements are built up to reduce the need for such scrutiny. Those patients expected to "terminate," as hospital language often puts it, are transferred to private parts of the ward; drapes around beds, while not completely concealing, are kept drawn most of the time, so that if a private room is not available, the larger ward type room is roughly reconstituted into a series of private rooms by the use of the curtains. This procedure, plus the generally ill status of most of the patients in those areas of the ward where death is likely to occur, makes the setting of these wards much less conducive to social interaction. The dangers of discovery which a history of sociable interaction between patients and an interest in the happenings of one's roommates would entail are thus minimized.

As I shall have occasion to note throughout, a great many of the arrangements at County are organized the way they are because of the general confinement of patients to beds and the general absence of relatives or members of the public at large in the hospital corridors. It is firm hospital policy that ambulatory patients be discharged from the hospital as soon after they become ambulatory as possible, so there are few patients wandering about in the halls. Patients requiring long-term care are typically transferred to the chronic care institution. The use of these inter-hospital transfers is very frequent. Occasionally, however, on the medical wards a recovering patient, one who is waiting his discharge from the hospital, will be seen walking back and forth on the corridors, chatting with nurses and aides. When such a patient is about, staff members make some slight efforts to monitor their conversational references to the deaths of patients, though not always consistently or successfully so. The morgue attendant often arrives at a nursing station to secure a deceased patient's chart, or the paper bag containing his personal belongings which will accompany his body to the morgue. On several occasions his requests, containing references to the fact of a death's occurrence, were made quite loudly, well within hearing range of the patients who happened to be standing near the station. On numerous instances nurses were observed to mention a patient's death when such a bystander was within range. While there would be no purposive reference to such matters in a patient's presence, the degree of care exercised in insuring the privacy of such talk is not always great. Ambulatory patients have been known, on occasion, to converse about the deaths of other patients with members of the staff, particularly lower echelon personnel like aides, orderlies and attendants who seem somewhat less concerned about the privileged character of the knowledge they have.

As a characteristic feature of County, the affairs of any given patient are not treated as particularly confidential, nor are their bodies treated with great concern for privacy. In the larger ward-type rooms, drapes are not always drawn about patients' beds during morning rounds so that, particularly on the male medical ward, a patient's body will often be well enough exposed for all in the room to see. The concern for privacy operates somewhat more consistently on the female medical wards, where whenever a woman's breasts or genitals are exposed, drapes are drawn around the bed. Female staff members seem to take greater care to insure that the modesty of patients (and perhaps their own) be respected than do male staff members. Among male staff members, the "visiting man" is characteristically that one among the collection of doctors at the bedside who gives the greatest attention to adequately drawing the drapes.

At Cohen Hospital, body exposure is much more seriously protected than at County, and conversation about a patient's

condition or a patient's death is usually restrained through
the use of a variety of anterooms and a more careful control
of voice pitch. It seems that the more the institution is open
to the public, the more elaborate and better enforced are its
arrangements for segregating front and backstage activities,
and for preserving the confidentiality of relations between
particular staff members and members of the family.

At Cohen when the private physicians converse with families, they lead them aside, form well-sealed gatherings, and
talk in hushed tones, giving respect both to the relatives'
own concern to keep family affairs family affairs and their
concern to keep their business from scrutiny by others.
The difference can be closely observed in the manner in which
the outcome of a surgical procedure is announced by the
physician to family members at Cohen and at County. At
County, family members await news of a surgical procedure
in that area of the Department of Surgery immediately adjoining the operating rooms. There are several benches in
this section where persons sit while their relatives are in
surgery. After the operation, doctors emerge from the operating rooms, and if they know the family, go to the bench
and speak to them. They will discuss the surgery while the
relative remains seated at the bench, even if several other
people can and do monitor the conversation. Should the
relative stand up when being addressed, as often happens,
the doctor will not lead him off to a private conversation
away from the bench, but will remain close to it. The doctor
indicates no special desire to regard the patient's condition
as a private matter of discussion. At Cohen, under such circumstances, the physician beckons the family aside and often
walks several feet away from others before beginning his
account. On one occasion, typical of many Cohen instances,
a doctor who announced the outcome of a surgical procedure
to the wife and brother of a patient was then asked to
"please come down and talk to Mama." He went to another

area of the floor where the elderly mother was waiting with
another family member; the old woman was given an account of the operation, in the course of which the doctor put
his arms around the woman, who was noticeably quite nervous, and offered comforting remarks.

The general pattern of nonprivacy and nonconfidentiality
which marks both conversation between doctors and relatives and conversations between staff members at County
has clear consequences for the general visibility of death and
death-related matters. From the standpoint of the investi-
gator, the location of death-related talk and death-related
equipment (morgue trays, death forms, etc.) was much
easier at County than at Cohen. The sheer likelihood of
hearing the word "autopsy" is greater at County, despite
the fact that the number of autopsies conducted is roughly
the same in both settings. On the County medical ward, it is
not infrequent to hear such interchanges as the following:

Doctor, from one end
of the ward to a doctor
at the other end: "I'm going to the morgue."

Nurse, to an aide, in
a large ward room: "Did they wrap Mrs. S. yet?"

Doctor to doctor, from
the nursing station to
the middle of the ward
corridor: "Did you pronounce him?"

Nurse, to another, in the
presence of a doctor-relative
encounter: "Did they get the autopsy permission?"

The general lack of a nonstaff public operates to instill a
general lack of concern for the audience of such remarks.
The transport of dead bodies at County is quite different
from the procedure used at Cohen. Let me address this mat-

ter in some detail, considering some especially interesting
aspects of the role of the key specialist in such activities.

THE MORGUE ATTENDANT

The arrival of the county coroner provides onlookers,
who know who he is, with clear information about the occurrence of a death. Another person, the morgue attendant
of the hospital, is particularly interesting as a similar source
of information. As in most hospitals, the County Hospital
morgue is located in a relatively inaccessible corner of the
hospital basement.[6] To reach it, one must take an elevator
to the basement from some point in the hospital, and walk
down a long underground corridor. At the far end of this
busy corridor, somewhat hidden around a corner, is the
morgue. There is no way to reach it except by passing the
plumbing, carpentry and electrical shops, the central supply
office, and the hospital laundry. There is one exception, and
that is a stairway that leads from the morgue area to the
Department of Pathology on the first floor. There is no elevator at that end of the building and bodies cannot be transported on stretchers to the morgue from that locale. This
stairway is used by professional personnel who prefer to
enter the morgue without walking the noisy and busy basement corridor, which is the province of blue collar workers.
The morgue attendant, among whose jobs it is to transport
bodies from the hospital wards to the morgue, on a typical
day makes several trips along this underground corridor,
pushing before him a stretcher, either empty or with a body
on top of it. Thus, the person who accepts a job as an ap-
prentice plumber in the hospital is likely to find that an object which he might have preferred not to see, is daily passed
before his eyes. While a dead body is tightly wrapped in a
sheet, and another sheet is employed to drape the entire
stretcher, it seems reasonably certain that nearly any on-

looker, adult or older child at least, would at a casual glance
see what is on the stretcher. The form of a body, an object
between five and six and a half feet in length, with bulges
at both ends and a rising area in the middle, is quite readily
discernible. Objects fitting that description are not easily
conceivable as other than human bodies, the more so perhaps given the fact that the setting is a hospital and a likely
place to find such objects, although this fact does not appear,
in my estimation, to be at all essential to make the identification.

On numerous occasions, the removal of a body was witnessed and from the gaze of onlookers one could detect that
it was a body which was being seen. Never has an onlooker
been observed to regard a sheet-covered body and not indicate in his glancing manner and subsequent activity that it
was a body he knew he had witnessed. When two or more
relatives, other visitors, or patients are with each other and
one of them witnesses what he takes to be a body while the
other has been looking away, the first very often brings the
other's attention to what he is seeing. There is often an interchange between them which gives the impression that the
passing object is being pointed out. When one person is alone
(particularly a nonstaff person) and sees what he takes to be
a body under the sheets of a stretcher, several characteristic
forms of reaction can be observed. The person turns away
in such a fashion as to indicate that he is not merely shifting
his attention but is turning away from something he has seen.
He does so abruptly, with a prior look at the body which
indicates that he is seeing a body and which makes the turn
away seem governed by that perception. Women have been
observed to cover their eyes, even when alone, and one
woman was seen to grow rather pale and faint-looking. Another was seen to begin a yell or gasp before she covered
her mouth.

Staff persons who prefer not to witness the transport of

bodies have available to them some systematic ways of placing themselves in a position so that they will not have to do so. In the hospital basement, an interesting practice was observed. The morgue attendant, on his way from the hospital morgue to the wards to retrieve a recently deceased patient, provided certain others with information that he was about to be so engaged, allowing them to plan their avoidance of his presence with the body. As he left the morgue to go to a ward, he took that route which he would follow on his return with the body, pushing stretcher before him. Along the basement corridor at County, each of several maintenance shops is so situated that it constitutes a mere recess in the corridor. From any point within one of these shops, one may always monitor the passing of people in the corridor. The morgue attendant explained that several of the men who worked in the maintenance departments characteristically used the fact of his appearance as a way of anticipating that a dead body would soon be pushed past them along the corridor. Some of them, upon witnessing him pass by with an empty stretcher, made sure that they would be so positioned that as he returned with the body they would have their backs turned to the corridor. In the plumbing department a man said that whenever he saw "John" go by to get a body he busied himself at his shelf so that when John returned with a body on the stretcher he would not be turned towards the corridor. The main door at the laundry room is a double Dutch door, the top half of which swings open. A woman is employed in that office whose task it is to receive laundry bundles and give receipts for them. Normally, the top half of the door is kept open. When John passes with his empty stretcher she closes it, anticipating his return. She remarked, "I just don't like to see them."

For those persons who knew John, his appearance alone, without the availability of specific information about "why he is here now," served others with a quite restricted range of interpretative possibilities. Upon seeing him anywhere in the hospital, it would be proper and not a way of joking to ask him, "Who died?" [7]

John was in a rather uncomfortable situation in his movements throughout the hospital. He was "trapped by his role." His chief and daily problem was going about the hospital without appearing to others as working. Persons who engage in occupations which, by virtue of the scope of the activities they engage in always appear "on the job," often attempt to disclaim the involvements others see in their presence. John found the hospital too small. Nearly everywhere he went, others could properly view his presence there as warranted by the occurrence of a death. He was viewed as either going to or having just come from such activities as picking up a body, or engaging in those gruesome parts of an autopsy in which others knew a morgue attendant to partake. In an important sense, particularly to the extent that others regarded him as somewhat ritually unclean by virtue of the activities he engaged in, he was like the proverbial man in a town too small to allow an indiscreet activity to go unnoticed.

John had problems such as how to engage in a sociable conversation (particularly with those women with whom he found some interest in cultivating a relationship), how to get someone to sit next to him, or not move away from him, in the hospital cafeteria, how to avoid interrogation by others about "what it is like" and how to enter any form of ordinary discourse without his affiliation with dead bodies intruding as a prominent way others attended him.

He attempted to convey a sense of not being at work, by developing clear styles for use when he wished to provide others a basis for disattending what they inferred his work-relevant attributes to be. His dress furnished one way to set apart his work from nonwork activities. Unlike many of the people who wear operating gowns to lunch in the staff cafeteria at County, John made it a habit to change from his gown (the same variety is used in the autopsy procedure as in surgery [8]) to the attendant's uniform before coming to lunch, even if he was to assist in an autopsy directly after lunch. He was the only attendant in the hospital who was ever seen to wear a shirt and tie, which he kept in his locker in the morgue for use on those occasions when he particularly wanted to become detached from his work. He was a good looking, athletically built Negro, who fancied himself as a man with the women in the hospital. On several occasions he was observed to change from his work gown into a shirt and tie in the middle of the day, to take a coffee break with one of the nurses in the lounge where men were permitted. By changing his clothes he attempted to convey a distance from his work activities, both temporally and physically. The bloodstains on a surgeon's gown, rather than being signs of messiness, are signs of closeness to a task, and in the case of surgery a considerably prestige-conferring task. Young physicians, particularly interns and first year residents, characteristically wore bloodstained gowns to the cafeteria, but older physicians did not. One first year resident was observed in the locker room of the surgical area to change from a clean to a dirty, bloodstained gown before going to lunch with a date. The bloodstains on a morgue attendant's gown also indicate closeness to a task, but one which, unlike surgery, brings the operator no particular prestige. Not only did John routinely change clothes before coming to lunch, but so did other staff members of the Department of Pathology.

A general strategy John employed was, upon meeting someone for the first time, giving an ambiguous account of his occupational tasks. Only if necessary and only after friendship was gained when friendship was sought, did he tell others that he worked in the morgue. A preferable account from his standpoint was "I work in the Department of Pathology," or even more detached from that scene, "I am an attendant." When he talked about his work he made a point of highlighting the interesting facts about it and de-emphasizing the grosser aspects such as moving bodies about, mopping the floor of a deceased's blood after an autopsy and those other matters which constitute the chief functions he performed.

While picking up a body from the ward, he worked quickly, taking no time out for conversation along the way, unless he could manage to leave his stretcher behind and use one off the ward to which he was going. Whenever he had a stretcher with him, empty or not, he avoided interaction with others, and they with him. One adaptation of his was to carry along with him a patient's file, or a log book, or some such item, when he was en route to get a body. Proceeding to the elevator with the body he characteristically engrossed himself in looking through whatever he had brought with him while he awaited the arrival of the elevator. This made him somewhat less available for visual encounters with others, with the attendant sense of unpleasantness he felt he provided them should they feel obliged out of acquaintance-ship or friendship to greet him. As he pushed his occupied stretcher, he always looked downward, and on numerous occasions persons with whom he was acquainted and to whom he would have otherwise made an overture of greeting and they the same to him, were silently passed by along his route.

One young nurses' aide, whom John reported he was dating, was seemingly not put off by the corpses he transported, and did not hesitate to engage him in conversation while he was with a body. He appeared uneasy in such conversations with her, and tended to nervously laugh about the scene of their engagement while it was in its course, indirectly pointing to what he tried to impress upon her as the impropriety of talking about sociable topics while in the presence of a

dead person (or to be so seen by others). On one occasion
she rested her hand upon the body while talking to him. He
got noticeably upset, apparently not so much because he
wouldn't do the same (he did in the confines of the morgue
and with persons who stood in similar occupational relationships to bodies as he did), but because he felt that as a public behavior this was in bad taste. Moreover, it didn't
provide for the kind of segregation between himself as a
handler of dead bodies and himself as a beau which he considered essential.

In his journey from the hospital ward to the morgue, he
would occasionally pass persons other than staff members.
At some hospitals, like Cohen, when a death occurs it is a
practice to close other patients' doors and try to clear the
corridors along which the body must be transported. There
is a hard and fast rule at Cohen that bodies are not to be removed from rooms during visiting hours. There is a similar
rule at County, but neither as hard and fast nor abided by
as consistently. At County, no special attempt is made to see
if anyone is on the ward before the body is removed from
the room and taken down the corridor to the elevator. As
for so many activities at County, here too the general absence of relatives and ambulatory patients is taken to make
such preparation relatively unnecessary. In a normal afternoon at Cohen, walking from one end of a floor to another
would entail passing numerous groups of patients visiting in
the halls with their families. At County such a walk will seldom involve passing such gatherings.

Should a nonemployee be on the elevator, an uncomfort-
ably extended containment of corpse and visitor in a small
place would occur. The attendant's procedure at the elevator is to stand outside it and wait until it arrives at his
floor unoccupied. While these elevators are officially designated for staff members' use, some of the visiting public,
what little there is of it, occasionally use them. At Cohen,

when a body is to be removed from a ward, an aide, orderly or nurse goes and gets an elevator, and only after it has arrived at the floor is the attendant signaled to wheel the body out into the hall and into the elevator. At County, the morgue attendant makes no such preparations, nor do other staff make them for him. Often he will stand in front of the publicly visible elevator entrance awaiting the arrival of the car for some time. Should the elevator arrive at his floor and a visitor be in it who is going on to a lower floor, the attendant makes a gesture indicating that he will await the car's return. Should the elevator arrive unoccupied or with a member of the hospital staff in it, he will wheel the body on and stand in front of it to prohibit any visitors from entering at a lower floor. These elevators, unlike some which hospitals use for such kinds of transportation, do not have devices whose actuation prohibits the elevator from being stopped by persons at floors along the route. John has the feeling that not all staff members should be made to ride downstairs with a body. On occasions he lets the elevator go by if a higher echelon physician or nurse is inside. When inside the elevator, should a doctor or nurse stop the car on a lower floor, en route to the basement, the morgue attendant gives the prerogative to the nurse or doctor as to whether or not they wish to ride with a body. He stands in front of the body and only steps aside, letting the nurse or doctor on, if they indicate they don't mind. If he feels they don't know that he is concealing a body and proceed to step on the car unknowledgeably, he calls the fact to their attention, with a remark like "I'm going to the morgue, sir," or "This is a body, sir," as he stands slightly aside to let them see what is behind him. Often doctors and nurses will say, "That's O.K., John," and board the car, but the hospital director and several others have been observed to refrain from riding with the corpse, by saying something like, "Oh, I'll catch it the next time." If a lower echelon person is awaiting

the car at a lower level, John will usually step aside and let
him ride down with him, if he wishes. When people arrive
at an elevator entrance and find John standing there with a
body, they frequently do not await a car, but walk down the
stairs, sometimes feeling obligated to announce that they
will do that with a remark like, "Oh, I think I'll walk,"
often followed by a politeness like, "How are things, John?"
On numerous occasions nonemployees were watched ap-
proaching an elevator to ride down to the main floor, and
upon seeing John with the body, turn away to proceed in
another direction, giving a sign that they had made some
sort of error, had lost their way, or otherwise attempting to
avoid open acknowledgement of anxiety about the contact.

Despite his attempts to structure his daily movements to
segregate his work tasks from his nonwork pursuits, a segregation which was difficult to perform by virtue of his
known-about activities and the encompassing character of
the hospital setting, John found that he could not completely dissociate his work from the moral character others
imputed to him by virtue of his being so employed. Even in
his nonwork hours in the hospital, when he found himself
able to engage in ordinary social discourse and could effectively appear as not currently engaged in work, he found
himself not especially well-liked. He commented that the
thing he found most uncomfortable about the job was not
the work which autopsies and body transportation entailed,
but the loneliness of that work.

Perhaps in compensation for the character of his job, both
its general gruesomeness and the social position it placed
him in, he was given a fairly decent salary, higher than any
other attendant or orderly in the hospital, and a fairly wide
latitude of authority in the conduct of morgue affairs. The
postmortem examination requires the work of two men. A
trained person is needed to do the major work of the exam-

ination. Another is necessary to prepare the body for autopsy, assist during the procedure and clean the autopsy
room afterwards. It is interesting to note that the morgue
is one of the few areas in the hospital where persons not involved in the medical training program may try their hand
at procedures normally performed only by those having
technical knowledge and skill which has been certified. Not
infrequently the morgue attendant at County began an
autopsy procedure himself. This involves making a large incision in the body from breastbone to pubic bone, and opening up layers of fat and muscle until the chest and abdominal cavities are exposed. While the morgue atendant is a
relatively skilled person by virtue of having witnessed hun-
dreds of postmortem examinations, he has no special training nor certification in surgical skills. John is known, among
pathologists at the hospital, for his expertise in "opening a
body," being particularly skilled in doing a cosmetically neat
job in removing the brain, a procedure which involves detachment of the skull in such a fashion that after the brain
has been removed from the head the skull cap can be replaced with no obvious sign of fitting unnaturally. This is a
man who has no high school education, the lower-class son
of a migrant worker. Yet he is quite conversant in the technical details of anatomy and matters pertaining to various
pathological conditions. As a "hobby" he reads surgical texts
and attends surgical operations. One physician, an assistant
resident pathologist, commented with intended exaggeration
but purported respect that "John knows as much pathology
as I do."

In Cohen Hospital, while the chief pathologist is the director of activities in the morgue, a young man, spoken of
as something of a "strange fellow," with an undergraduate
education is, in fact, in charge of coordinating many morgue
affairs. He is an avid student of disease and anatomy, and

keeps an impressive file on the pathological details of all deceased patients, not as part of his job, but for his own "interest."

While the law in some states requires that no parts of the body be permanently removed during autopsy, many parts are in fact not replaced in the abdominal cavity (the usual procedure after organs are examined), before the body is sewn up. Large amounts of tissue are kept for more detailed microscopic analysis, and occasionally, entire organs are permanently removed. Physicians often register their requests to study certain tissues, so that some opthamologists leave standing requests to obtain the eyes of all deceased, some urologists, the kidneys, and the pathologist, with permission of surviving relatives, stores these for specialists' research. At County, the morgue attendant went through a period of "study," moving from organ to organ. He kept these parts after autopsy and in his spare time dissected them and examined tissue under the microscope. The pathologist legitimated this procedure and recurrently instructed his staff to "be sure and save the —— for John."

Physicians are, in principle, expected to attend the post-mortem examinations on their own ex-patients whenever possible. Should a physician miss an autopsy, the morgue attendant is occasionally consulted to fill in details. Interns have been known to use the morgue attendant as a way of getting more detailed information than the laboratory report contained, particularly when they felt that they should be responsible for knowing that detail when "death rounds" were made each weekend, yet they could not be present at the examination themselves.

The morgue is thus a workable setting, a place where one, otherwise untrained, can achieve a measure of authority and learn a good deal, as a "hobby," about medicine and surgery.[9] In part, this is because there is little competition for these jobs. Pathologists are always pleased to find a worker who will handle many of the details of morgue work which they prefer not to encounter. In return for this help, the attendant is treated, within the morgue context at least, as a semistudent, one to whom it is legitimate to grant access to the use of microscopes, lab equipment, the scalpel and to whom instruction in a quasi-apprenticeship circumstance can be given. The pathologist at County feels that in treating the attendant as something more than an attendant, he can build interest into an otherwise unpleasant job, retain a good worker and insure that things get done which might otherwise be avoided or which he might have to do himself. What seems to happen is that work properly done by trained pathologists becomes defined as "dirty work." The opening of the brain, a rather crude process wherein the scalp is flapped over the face after the skull has been opened with a circular saw, is one of those autopsy procedures which appears sufficiently unpleasant that its conduct can be justifiably given over to the attendant. He is made to feel specially entrusted with a matter of importance while, actually, he is relieving physicians of the need to do such butchering themselves.

For years, at County, an older morgue attendant created considerable trouble for the department. He disliked, it was said, cleaning up after autopsies and engaged in systematic subterfuge to avoid having to partake in that procedure. It was said that he would often release bodies to morticians before the autopsy was conducted, by calling them on the phone and telling them that the relatives refused to allow a postmortem. When they came to get the bodies he released them, and on several occasions, apparently accounted for his behavior to the pathologist by putting blame on the funeral home, proposing that they insisted upon immediate release because the ceremony could not be forestalled any longer.

He was reportedly at fault for the development of a series of hostilities between hospital administrators and local mortuary establishments. His behavior was eventually discovered and he was dismissed from the hospital. John, all who knew him maintained, was a "conscientious worker."

IV

Social Death

When a patient's condition is considered such that he is "dying," or "terminally ill," his name is "posted" on the "critical patients' list." Once "posted," a patient has the theoretical right to receive visitors throughout the day and night rather than only at the appointed visiting hours. Posting also serves as an internally relevant message, notifying certain key hospital personnel that a death may be forthcoming, and that appropriate preparations for that possibility are tentatively warranted. In the hospital morgue, scheduling is an important requirement. Rough first drafts of the week's expected work load are made, with the number of possible autopsies being anticipated and planned for. In making such estimates the morgue attendant consults "posted lists" from which he makes a guess as to the work load of the coming week. The "posted list" is also consulted by various medical personnel who have some special interest in various anatomical regions. County's morgue attendant made it a practice to alert the ward physician that Doctor S., a research opthamologist, wanted to get all the eyes he could. To provide Dr. S. with the needed eyes, the morgue attendant habitually checked the "posted list" and tried, in informal talk with the nurses about the patient's family, to assess his chances of getting the family's permission to relinquish the eyes of the patient for research. Apparently, when he felt he had located a likely candidate, he thus informed the pathologist, who made an effort, via the resident physician, to have special attention given to the request for an eye donation. At several places in the hospital, on the admission nurse's desk, in the morgue, in doctors' lounges, and elsewhere, there were periodically placed signs which read, "Dr. S. needs eyes," "Dr. Y. needs kidneys," etc.

At County there is a Catholic chaplain whose main responsibility is administering last rites. Each morning he makes rounds through the various wards of the hospital. At each ward he consults a master schedule, which is an index file containing patients' names, religions, sex and diagnoses. All patients who have been posted are identified with a red plastic border which is placed on their cards. The chaplain goes through this file daily and writes down the names of all known Catholic patients who have been posted, whereupon he enters these patients' rooms and administers "extreme unction." After completing his round on each ward, he stamps the index card of the patient with a rubber stamp which reads:

Last Rites Administered
Date————Clergyman————

Each day he consults the files to see if new patients have been admitted to the wards and/or put on the critical list. His stamp serves to prevent him from performing the rites twice on the same patient.

In fact, many "posted patients" do not die, as "posting" is often done well before obvious impending death is noted. Therefore, quite a few people have the dubious honor of having left County alive, yet formally relieved of their

earthly sins. The priest reported that such cleansing is not
permanent, and that upon readmission to the hospital one
must, before he properly dies, receive last rites again as the
first administration is no longer operative.

It is significant that some "posted patients" can be properly regarded as candidates for autopsies before their
deaths, a conception which is not properly entertained at
Cohen Hospital. Indicative of the general stance taken toward some dying patients at County is the following conversation that occurred between two resident physicians at
the bedside of a "terminally ill patient" in the first stages of
a coma from uremic poisoning:

A: "Do you think, really, that both kidneys are as bad?"
B: "I know they're both bad because the output is so damned low.
Let's put it this way, neither one is good."
A: "Well, we'll find out for sure at autopsy."
B: "Right."

To discuss a patient's forthcoming autopsy, while the
patient is still a patient, would be severely sanctioned at
Cohen, without respect for the fact that the patient might
be considered "comatose" and not aware of conversation in
his presence. At County, there is a decided phasing-out of
attention given to "dying" patients, such that the possibility
of death within the period of a given work shift itself is
taken to warrant instituting certain forms of postdeath
treatment.

A tentative distinction can be made between "clinical
death," the appearance of "death signs" upon physical examination; "biological death," the cessation of cellular activity; and "social death," which, within the hospital setting,
is marked by that point at which a patient is accorded treatment essentially as a corpse, though perhaps still "biologically" and "clinically" alive. The following example is illus-

trative of what is intended by the term "social death:" A nurse on duty with a woman who she explained was "dying" was observed to spend some two or three minutes trying to close the woman's eyelids. This involved slowly but somewhat forcefully pushing the two lids together to get them to adhere in a closed position. After several unsuccessful moments she managed to get them to stay shut and said, with a sigh of accomplishment, "Now they're right." When questioned about what she had been doing, she reported that a patient's eyelids are always closed after death, so that the body will resemble a sleeping person. After death, she reported, it was more difficult to accomplish a complete lid closure, especially after the body muscles have begun to tighten and the eyelids become less pliable, more resistant, and have a tendency to move apart. She always tried, she reported, to close them before death while the eyes were still elastic and more easily manipulated. This allowed ward personnel to more quickly wrap the body upon death (if death indeed occurred), without having to attend cosmetic matters, and was considerate, she pointed out, of those who preferred to handle dead bodies as little as possible.

"Social death" can be said to be marked by that point at which socially relevant attributes of the patient begin to permanently cease to be operative as conditions for treating him, and when he is, essentially, regarded as already dead.

It is perhaps analytically tempting to conceive of social "death" as any instance of radically asocial treatment of a person, but such a usage would be, at the same time, analytically ambiguous, permitting such things as desertion by one's family and "nonperson treatment" to be so conceived. In keeping with the literal sense of "death," I intend a more delimited sense of "dead," where death is the warrantable basis for doing such things as planning an autopsy, disposing of personal effects, contracting mortuary institutions, putting a body in the morgue, informing insurance companies, remarrying, grieving, announcing the contents of a will, preparing obituary notices, transferring properties to another name, and generally, engaging in those organizational, ceremonial and economic activities which mark the end of social existence. Treatments or activities which often accompany the death of a person, or his "dying," but which accompany other kinds of states as well, are not specifically instances of "social death treatment," in my terminology. So the tapering off of visits on the part of relatives becomes an instance of "treatment as dead" when those activities which are substituted for visiting are properly substitutable only when the patient has already died. The distinction is not entirely unambiguous, but within the hospital setting, at least, a specific set of activities and treatments can usually be clearly located. When such activities occur, "social death" or "dying as a form of treatment" is said to occur, and whether that takes place before, concurrent with or well after actual biological" or "clinical" death is a matter for analysis.

A clear instance is seen in the circumstance where autopsy permits are filled out prior to death. For an autopsy to be performed, permission of the closest surviving relative must be obtained.[1] Two forms of permission constitute legally actionable documents: 1) a signature on a prepared "autopsy permission form" 2) a telegram from the surviving relative to the hospital, authorizing an autopsy. Obtaining an autopsy permit is regarded as a very important administrative necessity at the time of death. In order to qualify for AMA accreditation as a "teaching hospital," and thus be able to offer internships and residencies, a hospital must perform autopsies on 25 percent or more of the hospital's deceased patients. The minimum rate is not considered sufficient and most hospitals strive for as high a rate as possible. It is an apparently relevant question for a prospective resident to ask of the hospital "What is your autopsy rate?"

and for him to partially base his decision on where to do a residency on the basis of these rates.[2]

County's doctors attempt to obtain autopsy permission whenever possible, in part because they can be negatively sanctioned for not being concerned and for acting indifferently in this regard. When they expect that they will lose contact with a relative, they will, on those occasions where doing an autopsy is considered quite important (on a particularly interesting or diagnostically troublesome case), sometimes approach the relative of a patient who is considered to be "dying" and tactfully request that, "under the circumstances," a form be signed at the present time. At County this practice was employed only in cases where an autopsy was especially desired and then only if the relative had been made well aware that the patient was expected to die shortly.[3] There is the feeling that one can risk the possible sanctioning which such a proposal might incur only with either the very uneducated relative or the very sophisticated and emotionally cool one.

A typical instance of "social death" involved a male patient who was admitted to the Emergency Unit with a sudden perforation of a duodenal ulcer. He was operated upon, and for a period of six days remained in quite critical condition. His wife was informed that his chances of survival were poor, whereupon she stopped her visits to the hospital. After two weeks, the man's condition improved markedly and he was discharged in ambulatory condition. The next day he was readmitted to the hospital with a severe coronary. Before he died, he recounted his experience upon returning home. His wife had removed all of his clothing and personal effects from the house, had made preliminary arrangements for his burial with the mortuary establishment (she had written a letter which he discovered on his bureau, requesting a brochure on their rates), she no longer wore his wedding ring, and was found with another man, no doubt quite shocked at her husband's return. He reported that he left the house, began to drink heavily and had a heart attack.

PREPARATION OF THE CORPSE

A standard "death procedure" in nearly all American hospitals is the practice of "body wrapping." When a patient dies, the hospital "death procedures manual" instructs, his body is to be "wrapped" in a specially provided "Morgue Sheet." The body wrapping activity is apparently done nearly everywhere in United States hospitals in essentially the same fashion.[4]

At County, body wrapping is the work of aides and orderlies, over 95 percent of whom are Negroes. There is a legal regulation, purportedly instituted to protect the corpse from sexual attention, which requires that nurses' aides wrap female bodies and orderlies wrap male bodies. The sexual segregation of body care found in the handling of dead bodies is thus similar to that which governs some aspects of the care of live ones. There is also a regulation, at County as elsewhere, which requires that when a female body is removed from the ward to the hospital morgue by a male attendant, a nurse must escort it, this ruling being in some ways similar to that which requires a nurse's presence when a physician conducts a vaginal examination. Neither of these regulations is followed at County; male morgue attendants regularly transport female bodies by themselves, and male physicians do vaginal examinations without nurses being present. An exception to this absence of concern for sexual protection is in County's Emergency Ward where, in part because of the short-term character of doctor-patient relationships and the somewhat less clearly structured contractual relationship between the parties, such examinations are always done in the presence of a nurse. In this setting doctors have the fear that a woman will come for an examination just so as to stage the circumstances for a legal suit. The sex segregation of body wrapping appears to be chiefly a function of the fact that wards are segregated according to sex at County (an arrangement which does not exist at Cohen and is generally uncommon, I am told, in private hospitals), and orderlies are more commonly employed on the male wards and aides on the female wards.

Wrapping a body is a well-organized routine, having a characteristic temporal structuring, clear beginning, sequence of steps and closure. It is done collectively, by two or more persons, and is automatically carried off. When the technique is taught to initiates, it is taught as a complete ceremonial piece, like a variety of semiritualistic hospital routines which include preparing a patient for surgery, a woman for child delivery, etc.

On any given ward there is usually a team of aides or orderlies who work together in wrapping a body. They do the task systematically, with a certain degree of finesse, and prefer to work on it with those with whom they have done it before. When a new aide or orderly is introduced to the wrapping task he is asked to stand by and watch, as a narrative account of the procedure is given by one of the experienced members of the team. The procedure essentially involves the complete removal of the deceased's clothing, including all jewelry, and the folding of a heavy gauge muslin sheet completely around the body, pinning it down the front with large safety pins, in mummy style. Before the body is wrapped it is occasionally cleansed with a wet cloth, not thoroughly but only to remove any particularly noticeable dirt. A diaper-like sheet is wrapped around the genital area, the hands and feet are crossed and bound together with a special cotton-covered string. Two precut gauze pads are placed over the eyes, after the lids have been closed. Before the body is finally wrapped in the outside sheet, it is checked to make sure no paraphernalia is affixed to it. All IV tubes are removed, nasal suctioning equipment detached and catheters taken out.

In performing this task, aides or orderlies work in a co-ordinated fashion, indicating to the witness that the job has been done many times previously, and by the same team of workers. They start at one end of the body and work step-by-step until the procedure is finished. Typically, there is a division of labor, whereby one woman turns the body as the other spreads the sheet. This practice is institutionalized so that the same aide will typically do the same parts when working with her teammate.

The task is essentially secular in character; there are no explicit religious references made, although one aide charac-teristically hummed a Negro spiritual as she worked. What little talk takes place is relatively hushed in quality, with topics restricted to discussion of the patient. "She was a nice old woman, wasn't she?" "Yes, sure sorry to see her go." "She was pretty sick for a long time, I think." One senior aide, on every occasion as she inserted the last safety pin in place, patted the body on the thigh area and said, "Well, you're on your way now," whereupon she left the room. Nearly all women who have died in the female medical ward at County have received some variant of this last blessing. Generally, there is little conversation, with whatever occur-ring being sporadic rather than continuous throughout the course of the task. The whole job takes some fifteen min-utes, during all of which time the workers are busy. There are rarely any breaks taken in the course of the work. Once begun, it is carried through to completion, and if they do break they leave the room rather than take a break in the body's presence. Occasionally there is some joking, most of the occasions for which involve technical problems. In one instance, an aide stuck a safety pin too deeply, puncturing the skin and causing blood to appear and slightly stain the sheet. The other said, "Oh dear, guess we'll have to change the whole sheet," and the first answered, "She didn't feel nothin' though," and there was laughter.

The body is generally handled nonreverently by aides and orderlies. In turning it around to wrap the sheet, it is grabbed roughly and rolled over with none of the gentility which one observes in the rolling of live persons. One elderly nurses' aide found the generally rough treatment offensive and regularly said, throughout the course of doing a wrapping, "You shouldn't be so rough," addressing her helper, though to no great avail. Some personnel apparently take pride in the ease with which they manage what others might imagine to be the psychological discomfort of working with bodies. One aide, in demonstrating how bodies are wrapped to a new employee, took the young girl into a room where a patient had just been wrapped, and as she pointed to those features of the completed product which marked a good job, she made a point of ostensively showing what she meant, almost hitting the body at each point to demonstrate how tightly the sheet fit.

An orderly was instructing another how to affix the identification tags bearing the patient's name, age and sex, on the feet and at the midsection of the wrapped body (these tags are the same kind one uses in parcel post, the manila variety with a double wire at the end to tie the tag on with). As the novice fumbled in trying to put the tag on gently without having its wire touch the body itself, an occurrence which to a newcomer at such activities would be apparently too close to dead flesh for comfort, the old timer looked on with a developing smile. He interrupted the sweating novice with "Here, let me show you how," and quite forcefully, with exaggerated nonchalance, jabbed the wire through the feet section, seemingly trying, on purpose, to catch some flesh on the way, and said, "Don't be afraid of them, they don't feel a *thing* anymore." He laughed and the novice reciprocated with a nervous whimper.

Some parenthetical remarks about certain aspects of body care may be made here. In County, there is a clear division of labor and a clear difference in work styles with bodies. Physicians do not handle dead bodies except when they are pronouncing patients dead and conducting autopsies, and here their handling is limited strictly to the kinds of touch necessary for accomplishing these tasks. Gross body handling, movement of an entire body from one stretcher to another, from the morgue refrigerator to the autopsy table, is considered too much as dirty work for doctors, and is exclusively the province of the aides and orderlies. This differentiation of touching is common in handling live bodies as well, though not as markedly so as in the case of dead ones. When performing a physical examination on a patient a doctor will, if necessary, assist in turning a patient over to place him in a better position for the examination. If several physicians of differing statuses are jointly conducting an examination, as in "rounds," senior doctors will characteristically step back and allow the junior men access to the body to aid in turning it into position. With dead bodies, interns themselves maintain a generally aloof position. Once they pronounce a patient dead, they leave the room. In the morgue, an attendant himself positions the body on the autopsy table, and if he has difficulty in doing so physicians do not offer assistance. Here physicians limit their physical contact with the body to that which is required for doing the postmortem as a technical activity. In surgery, when a patient is being draped for an operation, an extended routine involving swabbing and the systematic laying of sheets, the junior physician of the operating team assists nurses while superordinate physicians stand by awaiting completion of the preliminaries. In the morgue, if physicians arrive in the autopsy room before the body has been transferred to the room from the adjoining refrigerator room, they often leave the morgue area entirely, with an instruction for the atten-

dant to ready the body. They adjourn to an office, and await
the attendant's announcement that everything has been readied. The pathologist, on several known occasions, scolded
the attendant for not having the body prepared for autopsy
when he knew one was scheduled.

On the wards, should a nurse have need to get something
from the room of a recently deceased patient, she will generally send an aide or orderly in to secure what she needs
rather than enter herself. Apparently a nurse feels she has
a right to properly keep her distance from involvement in
such activities as she might witness there. In witnessing body
work which occurs on a gross level, there is a sense in which
the witness thereby can become committed to the grossness
of the task, particularly so if witnessing involves one in informal talk with the workers. If one witnesses such activities
silently, he can assume the status of a mere witness, but in
engaging in talk in the same genre of that of the workers,
he gives others the impression that he is not being sufficiently concerned about what his higher status should require in the way of detachment.

Having briefly described the activity of body wrapping,
let me return to the main theme, the treatment of the "dying" patient. Despite the fact that it is routinely done, body
wrapping is regarded by aides and orderlies throughout the
hospital as an unpleasant task, and while these personnel
come to do it with no special fear, they do not look forward
to it. In fact, they systematically attempt to avoid the task.
One quite common device in County is to pretend that the
patient has not died, and if necessary and possible, to try to
camouflage his death by making him look alive. If they succeed, aides or orderies can manage to pass off the body for
the next shift which will discover the body and be responsible for wrapping it. The body is camouflaged by propping
the head up, closing the eyes to feign the appearance of
sleep, keeping intravenous solutions flowing, and screening

the body so that bypassing personnel will not notice the dead body. A more simple and common technique, particularly possible if the shift change will occur shortly, is to take a long coffee break, get involved in some other task and hope that co-workers will get called upon to wrap the body. These practices may be spoken of as instances of "clinical" and "biological" death before "social death," which is a less prevalent phenomenon at County than the reverse.

The wrapping task is also handled in an opposite fashion, this being one case where it is done in stages and not as an entire piece. What occasionally occurs here is that portions of the wrapping are done before death, leaving only a few moments of final touch up work with the dead body. This practice requires very knowledgeable personnel, those who can detect immediately forthcoming deaths with rather high accuracy. There is often one such person on any ward at any shift, and particularly on the medical wards where an employee gains a good deal of experience in judging such matters. On the male medical ward a nurse prided herself in the "fact" that she could predict, in many cases, which patients would die within the day, if any. A short-term check, by asking for her predictions each morning and checking them against actual deaths revealed that she approached a 75 percent degree of accuracy, and in several cases predicted the deaths of patients which doctors did not expect to occur as shortly as she said they would. If such a person is available, and aides can learn of her expectations, or themselves are good forecasters, they will occasionally go into the room of such a patient, change the bedsheets, insert dentures, and in several cases of which I know, diaper a patient who is still "alive." Such pre-death treatment is likely to occur only during the night shift when aides are assured that relatives will not visit and discover their work. When the patient dies, aides know that doctors will not examine the feet and discover the binding. If they do, as happened in one known case, the aides gave the account "right after he died we started on him." This practice is not officially sanctioned before the pronouncement of death, but is ordinary operating practice. Once the patient actually dies, all that remains to be done is tie the arms, and wrap the entire body, the more unpleasant matters, like diapering and replacing dentures having been taken care of previously. Care must be taken here lest the bedsheets become soiled again, though that possibility can be conveniently explained to be the result of post-death excretions.

Various other practices are designed to avoid or minimize the processing of a dead body, and these too involve pre-death treatment of persons as essentially dead. A very common one entails the "improper" use of interward transfers. A patient who comes into the Emergency Ward whose condition is such that his death is expected shortly, will occasionally be transferred to a medical or surgical ward, the presumed motive for which is that he is a terminally ill person and not properly a person for emergency care. The actual motive is suspected by the receiving ward's personnel to be the removal of a patient who is about to die so as to avoid having to care for his body. One evening, a patient in quite critical condition was transferred from the Emergency Ward over to the men's medical ward. The head nurse refused to accept the obviously dying patient, and complained that the Emergency Ward clerk simply sent him over to die on her property. She angrily instructed the orderly to return the patient to the Emergency Ward, with the message, "You tell Mrs. Smith to wrap her own bodies."

A very common example of "social death" before "actual" death involves the assignment of patients to beds. A patient who is admitted to the hospital in what is considered to be a near-death-state, with extremely low blood pressure, very erratic heartbeats and a nonpalpable or very weak pulse, is frequently left on the stretcher on which he is admitted, and put in the laboratory room, or large supply room. In such cases, a nurse explained, they don't want to mess a bed up, and that since the patient would soon die, there was no need to assign a bed (upon death, the complete bedding must be stripped, the room thoroughly cleansed, disinfected). In several cases, patients were left throughout the night to die in the supply room, and if in the morning they were still alive, nurses quickly assigned them beds, before the arrival of physicians and/or relatives. Here we see instances of movement back and forth between the statuses of life and death, with social life, at least as represented by a bona fide admission to the hospital bed, reinstituted after a night of treatment as a corpse. During a "death watch," the phrase used by nursing personnel to refer to guarding a dying patient in anticipation of his death, the patient is treated as in a transitory state, the relevant facts about him being the gradual decline of clinical life signs. As death approaches, his status as a *body* becomes more evident in the manner in which he is discussed, treated and moved about. Attention shifts more and more away from caring for his possible discomforts, and instituting medically advised treatments, to the sheer activity of "timing" his biological events. With a pre-death-coma patient, suctioning of the nasal passages, propping up pillows, changing bedsheets and the like, routinely occur as part of the normal nursing routine. As blood pressure drops and signs of imminent death are taken to be apparent, these traditional nursing practices become regarded as less important, and the major items of interest become the number of his heartbeats and the changing condition of his eyes. Suctioning activity diminishes in frequency, his position is not as regularly altered to insure more comfort and the surroundings are not kept in any particular state of cleanliness. On many occasions, nurses' aides were observed to cease administering

standing-order oral medications when death was expected
to take place within the hour.

The technical feasibility of phasing out the treatment of
dying patients is enhanced by the character of the ward's social structure. While "posted patients" theoretically have
the right to round-the-clock visitors, in actuality nurses strive
to separate relatives from those patients whose deaths are
regarded as imminent. They urge family members to go
home and await further news there, or insist that they wait
outside in the corridors and not in the patient's room. At
least part of their concern in doing so is to handle the forthcoming death within the context of other ward responsibilities. It is common for a patient to die unattended and be
discovered as dead considerably later, when a nurse, aide or
doctor happens into his room. One orderly refused, for the
first several weeks he was employed in the hospital, to wan-
der in and out of rooms, as an orderly must. He feared that
he wouldn't be able to manage himself should he come upon
a dead person. At County the occasion of a death is not particularly publicized on the ward, so that staff members are
not always forewarned that one has occurred. On one occasion, the lack of communication on the medical wards resulted in a rather unfortunate circumstance. A woman was
admitted to the female medical ward with severe vaginal
bleeding. Normally, such a patient would have been taken
to the obstetrics ward, but in this instance there were no
vacant beds on that service. In the course of her stay she
delivered a stillborn, extremely malformed infant. The
"baby" was wrapped in the traditional fashion and taken to
the morgue. During the evening shift, an elderly woman arrived on the ward and announced that she was the "grandmother" of the deceased baby. She was quite "hysterical"
and demanded to see the baby whom she claimed they "had
killed." After an argumentative few moments the head nurse
agreed to take her to the morgue and show the baby to her,

a procedure which, she explained, was highly irregular. They
went to the morgue, the nurse consulted the list of compart-
ment "occupants," and pulled out the tray containing the
stillborn. She unwrapped the sheet, exposing a horribly de-
formed creature, whereupon the "grandmother" fainted and
badly bruised her scalp. The nurse was furious for not having been informed of the baby's condition, and trembling noticeably, ran for help. A meeting was held the next day by
the medical nursing staff wherein it was agreed that thereafter every "report session" should make explicit mention
of all the day's deaths and review any particularly relevant
facts about them.

At County, relatives are infrequently present at the time
of the death. After a death occurs, the family is occasionally
asked by the physician who announces the death if they wish
to view the deceased. Very few relatives request to do so,
but should they, the procedure is that the body is to be
wrapped completely, with the exception of the head, which
is to be propped up on a pillow for display. On such occasions, the hospital stages a miniature ritual. An aide combs
the hair, fluffs the pillow and otherwise trys to simulate the
state of restful "repose" which morticians pride themselves
in accomplishing. For at least one such aide, the hospital experience in this and related tasks served as a practical intro-
duction to the mortuary profession, for which she left her
job at the hospital to prepare.

Should relatives request to view a body, the rule is that
the body be allowed to remain on the ward, prepared for
viewing, for no more than an hour after death. In fact, bodies stay around much longer. Staging a viewing is disruptive
of ward and hospital morgue activities. The body must be
specially wrapped with the head remaining exposed, the
nurse must go into the patient's room with the family in case
of an unmanageable scene and the morgue attendant must
forestall autopsy preparations. If an autopsy permit has

already been signed and it is in the morning when such procedures are normally performed, the morgue attendant will
try to get the nurse in charge to release the body before
viewing. Several occasions are known where this occurred,
and when relatives arrived to view the body they were told
that regulations had required that the body be removed
from the floor.

Typically, however, relatives are not in the hospital at the
time of the death and generally, they do not request to see
the deceased. Before death, with relatives continuously present in the "dying" patient's room, a more constant vigilance
over the patient's condition must be maintained, requiring
in effect the removal of a nurse from other activities to spend
her exclusive time at the bedside. The routine handling of
death as it occurs in a matter-of-fact fashion on the medical
wards at County, requires that the ward be kept relatively
free of outsiders, whose mere presence exacts greater de-
mands on the behavior of staff than the likelihood of a death
would normally warrant. Discovery, or even simultaneous
discovery of the death by relative and physician, or relative
and nurse, is considered something to be avoided. While the
justification for shielding off dying patients from relatives
is made in terms of the "unpleasantness of seeing someone
die," the fact that such shielding does not always occur in
other kinds of hospitals (like Cohen, where relatives are
considered specially entitled to be present at the bedside
when the patient "expires"), seems to point to the character
of hospital routines in these different settings and the organization of "death care," as the crucial basis for this practice. At County, pre-death body treatment can occur as it
does only if family members are kept away, and a phasing
out of attention is allowable so long as the family is not able
to witness or to infer it.

The physician too, at County, prefers that relatives be
kept away from the bedside of a dying patient, so that he is

freer to leave the bedside himself and attend to other matters. This concern operates particularly strongly during late
evening hours, when the sheer fact of a dying patient on his
service would not ordinarily be taken to require his continuous presence. With respect to most of his "dying" patients,
the physician regards the forthcoming death matter-of-
factly, and feels no special discomfort in the fact that no one
is actually on hand when it takes place. The absence of relatives on the ward, and especially at the bedside, allows him
to wait until a more reasonable hour to come to the ward to
pronounce a patient dead and then inform the relatives of
the death. In many instances a patient is discovered dead in
the midst of the night and the doctor not informed of the
death until the morning. Physicians often express anger at
nurses who awaken them at night because of the death of
one of their patients.[5] It routinely happens then that a patient will die while a doctor is not on the ward, and remain
"unpronounced" until the physician finds it suitable and convenient to come in. The absence of relatives at close proximity to the bedside further allows nurses to avoid calling
the doctor in charge until they themselves are about to leave
the shift. This way they can assist their aide staff in passing
on the body for the next shift. One of the disadvantages of
the daytime shift, from the perspective of nurses and aides,
is the greater likelihood of having to remove several bodies
upon their arrival at work. They themselves find it less easy
to pass a body on to the evening shift, due to the great activity of the daytime shift, the movement back and forth
of patients and doctors and the need for bedspace for new
admissions, and thus the greater likelihood of discovering a
body and the greater difficulty of concealing one. Of course,
the night shift cannot pass every body on to the day shift,
because it becomes quickly obvious that not all nighttime
deaths occur after 6:30 A.M. Some effort is made to random-
ize the recorded death times, but the night shift always man-

ages to get away with fewer bodies to wrap than any other shift, even though the distribution of reported deaths, by hours, is apparently random in the long run.

Discovering a dead patient typically occurs in the course of ongoing ward activity. Most patients die unattended at County, largely because of the nature of the care accorded them when they reach what is considered to be the "dying" stage. In encountering those patients whose death is considered imminent, experienced personnel manifest a characteristic stance of caution, lest the patient already be dead and that fact not noticed. As nurses make their rounds, they periodically check up on "dying patients." This check involves a long stare from the door to see if the patient is breathing (some middle-class mothers are known to do the same with their new infants, but the basis for so doing seems quite different in the two cases). The nurse's chief concern is to detect death shortly after it occurs so as to institute proper preparations to remove the body from the ward quickly, insure that her subordinate personnel do not neglect their responsibilities. While aides seek to avoid making such discoveries, in part because of the fact that they are the ones directly implicated in the body's care, most nurses, with the exception of a few alienated ones, are concerned to insure that such discoveries are promptly made. It is considered relatively disastrous for a young student nurse to unwittingly treat a dead person as though he were still alive, yet on several occasions, newer personnel have had such experiences. In one case a man was being attended who had been severely burned and was nearly totally wrapped in gauze, with the exception of his eyes. A young student spent several minutes trying to get him to drink some juice through a straw, and having no success, she reported to her instructor for help. The instructor said, "Well, honey, of course he won't respond, he's been dead for twenty minutes." When the student gathered herself together she explained that all she "could see was his eyes and they had always been closed." Another young student, carefully following her routines from bedside to bedside, spent several moments changing the bedsheets of a patient who had just died. Another carefully suctioned the nasal passages of a deceased patient. Still another gave a deceased patient an injection. For one who is even slightly experienced in witnessing and handling the dead, the likelihood of such occurrences seems quite rare. However, unless one attends the possibility that he is handling a dead person, death's occurrence may go unnoticed, the more so it seems as the procedure one performs is done in a perfunctorily routine manner. Such occasions are regarded seriously and not usually taken as warranting humor. The student nurse who was told the patient she had just injected was already dead, cried nervously and trembled for several minutes; she was given a half hour off to recover from her distress.

While such occurrences are empirically uncommon, their possibility seems somewhat enhanced by the fact that the general notion of "being in a coma" operates as it does. So-called "comatose" patients are treated as essentially dead. Considering a person in a coma is warrant for talking about him in his "presence" in ways which would not be permissible were he awake (this perhaps distinguishes the comatose and anesthetized person treatment from true "nonperson treatment," treatment of a person as not present even though he is sensibly on the scene and capable of monitoring what goes on conversationally [6]).

There is apparently some question as to whether verbal interchange is accessible or not to the "comatose" patient, for some such patients, those who live through the "coma," are known to have reported scattered detail of things said in their presence.[7] In County, however, the "coma" is considered equivalent to general anesthesia in its effects, and patients' conditions and prospects are freely discussed in

their presence when they are felt to be "comatose." Such an
an assessment is made when the patient does not respond to
verbal or physical stimuli, and the possibility that nonrespon-
siveness may be an inability to respond to, rather than receive stimulation, is not seriously entertained.

In dealing with comatose patients, a high proportion of
County's critically ill population, personnel become accus-
tomed to disattending the patient as a social object, so much
so that the fact that the patient might already be dead may
occasionally slip by unnoticed. Since pre-death treatment as
a corpse extends backward in time to include many comatose
patients, there is, in actual practice, little distinction between
the comatose and the dead. A patient "dies," in some important organizational respects, once he enters what is taken
to be a terminal coma, and death itself is not radically
marked by a special attitude toward the body, or at least as
much so as that which it evokes when it occurs suddenly,
with no transitory period of "dying in a coma." Far and
above, the greatest number of deaths which occur at County
and at Cohen are deaths which are preceded by a period
which is generally regarded as a coma. Of some two hundred
deaths observed, no deaths of the Hollywood version,
wherein the person's last sentence is interrupted by his final
breath, have been observed.[8]

The noncomatose patient who is expected to die on the
current hospital admission cannot be the object of pre-death
treatment as a corpse until the coma itself is entered. In
these patients' presence, talk about their prospects is camouflaged by the use of a special descriptive language which it
is taken the patient cannot decipher. In the presence of a
woman who was expected to die within a week of uremic
poisoning, one physician said to a nurse, "She'll probably
terminate this week." The patient, a very anxious Negro
woman who may have detected the relative somberness of
the physician's mood and the general seriousness of her

state, nervously asked, "Am I alright, doctor?" The physician answered, "Yes, Mrs. K., you're doing just fine."

PROGNOSTICATIONS OF DYING

As an acute treatment hospital, the average length of stay at County is less than ten days. This means that of the patients who die in the hospital, quite a few have never engaged in social interaction with doctors and nurses, or their family members, during the course of this final hospital admission. Unlike the circumstance of long-term, chronic-care facilities in private institutions where patients can afford prolonged treatment and where physicians have a greater stake in the outcomes of their patients' illnesses, patients at County Hospital are discharged from the hospital as soon as they show capability of being able to make it on their own. It is hard and fast policy to keep the patient population circulating as much as possible. While the average stay for a heart attack victim at Cohen Hospital frequently exceeds four weeks, the same kind of patient will seldom spend more than twelve days at County, even though he may be back in the hospital many more times in the course of a year than the Cohen patient.

Of some two hundred deaths witnessed, only a dozen or so involved patients who had had previous interaction with the members of the hospital staff; all the rest were "far enough along" in their illnesses to be in comatose condition from the time of entry into the hospital up until their deaths. The greatest proportion of deaths occur within three days after the person's admission to the hospital.

The timing of proclamations of "dying," or "terminality," made both among staff members to each other and to the families of patients, is more or less crucial depending upon the way those who make such proclamations, or undertake treatment on the basis of an expectation of death-this-time, have their activities scrutinized by others, including the family.[9] Before a body will be "pre-wrapped," before it will be kept overnight in a treatment room rather than be assigned to a bed or before autopsy permission will be sought prior to death, ward personnel must feel as though they have quite firm reason to believe the patient's death is extremely close in coming. "Dying," as such procedures, awaits the final moments.

Yet the notion of "dying" extends beyond such forms of body treatments per se, to include the relevance or not of instituting treatments to forestall death. Noncurative treatment, which can be assembled under the general heading of "palliative care" (or "terminal care" as it is sometimes called) is to be distinguished from what is generally spoken of as "euthanasia" which, in its typical conception, involves the purposeful termination of life through some active intervention so as to shorten a painful period of dying.[10] Instances of this "pure-form" euthanasia were not found at County. But "palliative care," negatively defined by the admitted suspension of curative medical treatments and positively by the admitted concern to treat pain only, is commonplace. The institution of "palliative care" is one important practical consequence of regarding a patient as "terminally ill" at County. Insofar as the suspension of curative medical treatments, or treatments designed to prolong life, may have, as an effect, the shortening of life, then "dying," as a warrant for this shortening of life, may take on the character of a "self-fulfilling prophecy," to use a familiar phrase.

From the physician's standpoint, a case ceases to be "medically interesting" in the comatose, pre-death stage. Once "palliative care" is instituted, diagnostic enthusiasm becomes less sustainable. The care of such patients is considered as essentially a matter for nursing personnel and physicians lose their interest in the patient. When that point is reached and the likelihood of an improvement of condition is considered negligible, the activities of diagnosis and consequent treatment lose, for the intern and resident in training, one of their key functions, namely, their ability to allow him to demonstrate his technical competencies and engage in semi-experimental learning ventures.

No matter how firmly grounded the physician's assessment of inevitable death, and no matter how deteriorated and beyond repair the patient's condition, the reluctance or willingness to treat the patient as one who is dying can be often located by reference to the pressures which confront the physician, and particularly by reference to the extent and manner in which he finds his activities accountable to others. Within the course of a hospital admission which is felt to be the patient's last, the timing of the proclamation, or if not an outright proclamation then the institution of "merely palliative care," can be seen as largely a function of the various audiences which the physician faces and attends as audiences he might be obliged to face.

In the course of their daily business, physicians engage in premising medical courses of action on the basis of diagnostic and prognostic assessments of the patient's medically defined circumstances. They are held to account, or potentially held to account, within the organized medical profession by rules of certification, within the hospital by the sanctioning mechanisms available to their superiors, peers and subordinates, and by the public through the resources of the legal system and mechanisms of public opinion and preferences, for the competencies they demonstrate in programming courses of treatment. The occurrence of a physician's patient's death can often be a key focal point for considering the operation of these varying sanctioning systems.

The ideal circumstance of death, from the physician's standpoint, is death which results from "dying," when "dying" means the operation of some locatable, "fatal process" which can be prospectively, properly spoken of as the thing "which will cause it." The ability of the physician to "discover dying," as this "process," and prospectively announce that discovery, provides him with a way of locating the "cause" of the death such that he can disclaim his own personal responsibility and the responsibility of the medical discipline for the death.

The least comfortable circumstance of death, from the doctor's perspective, is when it occurs and there has been no predictive statement of its possibility in advance. Here the physician is in the situation of possibly having to confront accusations of his own incompetence and that, in turn, may establish the conditions under which he, rather than a disease's inevitable, natural operation, can potentially be considered as material in the occurrence of the death.

A central concern of the physician is to attempt to minimize the likelihood of the latter variety of death by providing, wherever possible, that others will regard death as always possible, even though no specific basis for its possibility, such as a disease or other causally adequate and appropriate category, is located. While seeking to institutionalize something of a general air of pessimism, at the same time the physician must be careful not to convey to others the sense that in regarding death's likelihood thusly he is adopting a seemingly fatalistic stance toward recovery and the success of treatment. An important category for him to establish as a way in which others will attend his activities by way of the patient's performance is "possibly dying." The character of the language of medical prognosis can be analyzed as partially structured to establish the relevance of that category.

County physicians continuously concern themselves with having their prognostic conversations with patients' relatives convey a proper degree of solemnity. The general problem can be posed as follows: the physician must attempt to present a description of the patient's condition so that in the event of a death, the family will retrospectively regard his own activities and attitude as having been warranted. The physician who tells the members of his patient's family that there is likely to be a death can find himself in the uncomfortable situation of having to reencounter them on each of a series of successive days with much the same news, despite the fact that the patient continues to live. Unless the doctor has fairly sure expectations that death is immediately forthcoming, he will not employ "dying" as a way of posing the patient's condition, out of a concern that the patient, in living for a longer period of time than he expects, will provide relatives with a basis for saying the doctor made and acted upon a premature estimation of forthcoming and inevitable death, and had he treated the patient with an eye toward effecting a cure, death might not have occurred. Proclamations of inevitable death must thus be made at a well-timed point, unless it were the case that "dying" could be proposed as a reversible process. It seems to be the case that persons attend the notion "dying," in County at least, as a description of a state of affairs which is nonpreventable. Once personnel use the term, they intend by it to point to the expectation that death will occur within the course of the present admission. If they intend to point to a situation of possible death they employ other terms.

On several occasions, premature proclamations of inevitable death resulted in embarrassing situations. An intern informed a family that their father was "dying" and the father continued to live for over a week. Each day, sons, daughters and grandchildren came to visit the patient and each member of the family took turns going into his room to have a last look at "papa." A son served as a ritual leader each evening, standing outside the door to the room and scheduling the visits so that each member of the family would have his turn. This went on for several days, and as

time progressed the finality of their visits became questionable. Those relatives who had made what they thought to
be a final farewell, found themselves returning to the hospital and reentering the room again and again. Soon the ritual seemed to degenerate through a lack of closure. On the
sixth such day, the son requested to see another physician
and, it was reported, offered a cautiously voiced complaint
because it seemed to him that his father was indeed not dying, yet being apparently treated as though he were. The
intern was advised by his superiors of the tactlessness of his
premature announcement to the family. Things had
stretched out a bit too long so that he had provided for the
relevance of pre-death bereavement when it wasn't apparently relevant. "Fortunately" perhaps, for the intern, the
man died on the seventh night in the hospital.

Just as proclamations of inevitable death must not be
made too prematurely, they must neither be made too close
to the point of the death, for then, with death following
quickly after the expectation of it, the physician has less time
in which to transfer the patient's fate from the world of
medicine and his own hands, to those of "God." Death must
be made to seem an outcome of "dying," as an inevitable
transitory status, for without such a transition, death loses
its apparent naturalness and becomes open to interpretation
as a wrongly caused affair. A striking instance of planned
sequencing was reported to have occurred in the operating
room. A patient was operated upon for a gunshot wound,
which was not apparently considered serious enough to warrant preparing the family for the prospect of possible death.
He died on the operating table, and rather than deliver the
news of the death forthrightly, the operating team was reported to have decided to create a sense that "dying" preceded death by filtering out news of progressive deteriora-
tion in the patient's condition, after he had already died. On
each of several occasions, a member of the team encountered

awaiting family members with increasingly poorer news of the operation's progress and the patient's health. After several progressively more solemn prognostications, the occurrence of death was announced, now placed within a history of "dying."

In the circumstance of DOA deaths in the Emergency Ward, doctors who announce the death often do so in such a way as to suggest that "dying" preceded it, by saying, "Well, apparently your husband had a bad heart attack this morning and that was probably something he was predisposed to have," or "From the looks of things he was in bad condition in the past. . . ." This is a situation where accountability is realistically minimized. The doctor does not know the "patient" nor the relatives, yet he feels obliged to suggest a natural sequence of prefatory illness.

Physicians generally seek to avoid the necessity of such frantic, last minute historicizing, by providing that form of prognostic account which will leave open the possibility of death without directly suggesting it and thereby risking premature pessimism to be interpreted in their actions. This is typically accomplished through gradual shifts in the tone of prognosis, whereby the attempt is made to keep open the various contingencies which might occur, never making a definite commitment. The progressive solemnization of prognostic accounts as the patient's condition deteriorates goes as follows: on early days of admission of the patient who is considered as a possible eventual death, he is talked of as "in serious condition;" as his death becomes considered more immediately imminent, references to it being "a matter of time" are made. References to "dying" are cautiously made only when the final moments are considered to be at hand. The use of such phrases as "only time will tell," "we've done all we can," "it's just a matter of waiting to let nature take its course," "there's no telling now," provide that should the patient die, "dying" will have been seen as having gone on beforehand, at the same time, should the patient live through the admission, the doctor's competence is not thrown into question, but perhaps enhanced. It is always to the physician's advantage to portray the situation as slightly more serious than he feels it is, so long as its seriousness is not taken or proposed as a warrant for treating "palliatively."

The structure of County Hospital's pattern of family visiting and its typical population of relatives provide an organizational basis for handling some of the problems in structuring prognostic talk. One fact of relevance is that relatives are infrequently present in the hospital, so that, quantitatively speaking, there is little contact between physician and relative. A goodly number of County's patients are without families or have families only nominally but not actually responsible. In County, as in other such lower-class institutions, accountability vis-a-vis the family is not seriously attended by physicians. With a lack of historical involvement between physician, patient and relative, the hospital is not regarded, either by members of lower-class society or by the hospital staff, as an arena to which the traditional doctor-patient relationship moves from the office. "Going to the hospital," in lower-class society, seems to mean giving oneself up to the care of an institution, more so than it is viewed as a step continuous with other modes of medical care. Many County patients have no "private physicians." When in the hospital, patients are treated by many doctors who interchange with one another in caring for their needs. Seeking a physician to learn of a relative's physical condition is frustrating, in that a physician often cannot be located. The doctor one sees one day is "off duty" the next.

The general pattern of relative visiting, the interchangeability of personnel and the lack of doctor-patient-relative relationship serves to allow the institution of "palliative care" and the enforcement of an attitude of inevitability at

an early stage in the admission of a semi-comatose or comatose patient. That a patient initially considered to be "dying"
might survive a given admission is less a potential source of
embarrassment and potential sanctioning to the extent that
relatives are not around to inquire into their relatives' progress. In a medical conference, a case was raised which illus-
trates one way in which accountability is regarded as a
constraint upon premature remission of serious diagnostic
attention and curative treatment.

A woman was admitted to the hospital in a very weak condition with what were described as complaints of listlessness,
nausea, fever and severe loss of weight. She was seventy-
seven years old and had a history of recurrent diabetic difficulties and one previous heart attack. It was suspected, on
the basis of a preliminary blood test, that she had developed
a lymphosarcoma which may have been involved in a more
extended cancerous development. In the course of the conference a decision had to be made as to whether or not to
perform an extended series of tests to solve this rather ambiguous diagnostic situation. One physician argued that he
was convinced a diagnosis of "leukemia" was warranted,
and was prepared to make a prognosis of forthcoming death
on that basis. Another felt less secure about that diagnosis
and argued for a more complete series of tests and the temporary suspension of further treatment until a more specific
diagnosis was obtained. The family's stake in learning of
the illness was then discussed. After learning that the woman's husband visited her only once during the period of the
week in which she had been hospitalized, and that he had
been drunk at that time, it was agreed that, since she was
so "sick," and that her diabetes was acting up again, it
"didn't pay," as one of them put it, to bother with the additional tests. They decided to wait and see what happened
for several days, to see if she became markedly worse, and
if nothing happened, to then order more tests. The fact of

her husband's absence was stated to be a chief consideration
for not rushing to make a diagnosis. His lack of concern was
admittedly taken to warrant theirs, at least to the extent
that she would be allowed to deteriorate further, if she
would, before more extensive diagnostic work was pursued.
If she got worse and approached death, they agreed, there
would be no point in worrying more about the diagnosis. If
she didn't become more ill, they would wait to see that development, and then attempt to uncover a more secure diagnostic basis for instituting treatment.

This situation of choice, whether or not to take full efforts to treat quickly or adopt a "wait and see" attitude, is
extremely common in the "care" of patients who are regarded as potential candidates for the week's tally of deceased patients. The "wait and see" attitude is deemed
legitimate by County's interns and residents when there is
reason to believe that death is a distinct possibility. It pro-
longs the need for extensive diagnostic attention which, with
these patients, is considered warranted only if they are so
located in the age and social structure that life is considered
especially worth preserving. I shall examine the role of
deemed social worth in programming medical courses of action and talking of "dying" and "death" by considering the
circumstance of the "DOA" patient, for it is here that certain such decisional matters are rather clearly delineated.

V

Death, Uses of a Corpse, and Social Worth

In County's Emergency Ward, the most frequent variety of death is what is known as the "DOA" type. Approximately forty such cases are processed through this division of the hospital each month. The designation "DOA" is somewhat ambiguous insofar as many persons are not physiologically dead upon arrival, but are nonetheless classified as having been such. A person who is initially classified as "DOA" by the ambulance driver might retain such a classification even though he might die some hours after his arrival at the hospital.

When an ambulance driver suspects that the person he is carrying is dead, he signals the Emergency Ward with a special siren alarm as he approaches the entrance driveway. As he wheels his stretcher past the clerk's desk, he restates his suspicion with the remark, "possible," a shorthand reference for "Possible DOA." The use of the term *possible* is required by law which insists, primarily for insurance purposes, that any diagnosis unless made by a certified physician be so qualified. The clerk records the arrival in a log book and pages a physician, informing him, in code, of the arrival. Often a page is not needed as physicians on duty hear the siren alarm and expecting the arrival wait at the entranceway. The "person" is rapidly wheeled to the far end of the ward corridor and into the nearest available foyer or room, supposedly out of sight of other patients and possible onlookers from the waiting room. The physician arrives, makes his examination and pronounces the patient dead or alive. A nurse then places a phone call to the coroner's office, which is legally responsible for the removal and investigation of all DOA cases.

Neither the hospital nor the physician has medical responsibility in such cases. In many instances of clear death, ambulance drivers use the hospital as a depository for disposing of a body, which has the advantages of being both closer and less bureaucratically complicated a place than the downtown coroner's office. The hospital stands as a temporary holding station, rendering the community service of legitimate and free pronouncements of death for any comers. In circumstances of near-death, it functions more traditionally as a medical institution, mobilizing lifesaving procedures for those for whom they are still of potential value, at least as judged by the ER's staff of residents and interns. The boundaries between near-death and sure-death are not, however, altogether clearly defined.

In nearly all DOA cases, the pronouncing physician, commonly that physician who is the first to answer the clerk's page or spot the incoming ambulance shows, in his general demeanor and approach to the task, little more than passing interest in the event's possible occurrence and the patient's biographical and medical circumstance. He responds to the clerk's call, conducts his examination and leaves the room once he has made the necessary official gesture to an attending nurse (the term "kaput," murmured in differing degrees of audibility depending upon the hour and his state of awakeness, is a frequently employed announcement). It happened on numerous occasions, especially during the mid-night-to-eight shift, that a physician was interrupted during a coffee break to pronounce a DOA and returned to his colleagues in the canteen with, as an account of his absence, some version of "Oh, it was nothing but a DOA."

It is interesting to note that while the special siren alarm is intended to mobilize quick response on the part of the ER staff, it occasionally operates in the opposite fashion. Some ER staff came to regard the fact of a DOA as decided in advance, and exhibited a degree of nonchalance in answering the siren or page, taking it that the "possible DOA" most likely is "D," and in so doing gave authorization to the ambulance driver to make such assessments. Given that time lapse which sometimes occurs between that point at which the doctor knows of the arrival and the time he gets to the patient's side, it is not inconceivable that in several instances patients who might have been revived died during this interim. This is particularly likely as apparently a matter of moments may differentiate the reviveable state from the irreversible one.

Two persons in "similar" physical condition may be differentially designed as dead or not. For example, a young child was brought into the ER with no registering heartbeat, respirations or pulse and was, through a rather dramatic stimulation procedure involving the coordinated work of a large team of doctors and nurses, revived for a period of eleven hours. On the same evening, shortly after the child's arrival, an elderly person who presented the same physical signs, with what a doctor later stated, in conversation, to be no discernible differences from the child in skin color, warmth, etc., "arrived" in the ER and was almost immediately pronounced dead, with no attempts at stimulation instituted. A nurse remarked, later in the evening: "They (the doctors) would never have done that to the old lady (attempt heart stimulation) even though I've seen it work on them too."

During the period when emergency resuscitation equipment was being readied for the child, an intern instituted mouth-to-mouth resuscitation. This same intern was shortly relieved by oxygen machinery and when the woman "arrived," he was the one who pronounced her dead. He reported shortly afterwards that he could never bring himself to put his mouth to "an old lady's like that."

It is therefore important to note that the category "DOA" is not totally homogeneous with respect to actual physiological condition. The same is generally true of all deaths, death involving, as it does, some decisional considerations, at least in its earlier stages.

There is currently a movement in progress in some medical and lay circles to undercut the traditional distinction between "biological" and "clinical" death, and procedures are being developed and their use encouraged for treating any "clinically dead" person as potentially reviveable.[1] This movement, unlike late nineteenth-century arguments for life after death, is legitimated by modern medical thinking and technology. Should such a movement gain widespread momentum, it would foreseeably have considerable consequence for certain aspects of hospital social structure, requiring, perhaps, that much more continuous and intensive care be given "dying" and "dead" patients than is presently accorded them, at least at County. At Cohen Hospital, where the care of the "tentatively dead" is always very intensive, such developments would more likely be encouraged than at County.

Currently, at County, there seems to be a rather strong relationship between the age, social backgrounds and perceived moral character of patients and the amount of effort which is made to attempt revival when "clinical death signs" are detected, as well as the amount of effort given to forestalling their appearance in the first place. As one compares practices at different hospitals, the general relationship seems to hold, although at the private, wealthier institutions, like Cohen, the overall amount of attention given to "initially dead" patients is greater. At County, efforts at revival are admittedly superficial, with the exception of the very young and occasionally wealthier patient, who by some accident, ends up at County's ER. No instances have been witnessed, at County, where external heart massage was given a patient whose heart was stethoscopically inaudible, if that patient was over forty years of age. On the other hand, at Cohen Hospital heart massage is a normal routine at that point, and more drastic measures, such as injection of adrenalin directly into the heart, are not uncommon. While these practices are undertaken for many patients at Cohen if "tentative death" is discovered early, as it generally is because of the attention "dying" patients are given, at County they are reserved for a very special class of cases.

Generally, the older the patient the more likely is his tentative death taken to constitute pronounceable death. Before a twenty year old who arrives in the ER with a presumption of death, attached in the form of the ambulance driver's assessment, will be pronounced dead by a physician, very long listening to his heartbeat will occur, occasionally efforts at stimulation will be made, oxygen administered, and oftentimes stimulative medication given. Less time will elapse between initial detection of an inaudible heartbeat and nonpalpable pulse and the pronouncement of death if the person is forty years old, and still less if he is seventy. As well as can be detected, there appeared to be no obvious difference between men and women in this regard, nor between white and Negro "patients." Very old patients who are considered to be dead, on the basis of the ambulance driver's assessment, were seen to be put in an empty room to "wait" several moments before a physician arrived. When a young person is brought in as a "possible," the ambulance driver tries to convey some more alarming sense to the arrival by turning the siren up very loud and continuing it after he has already stopped, so that by the time he has actually entered the wing, personnel, expecting "something special," act quickly and accordingly. When it is a younger person that the driver is delivering, his general manner is more frantic. The speed with which he wheels his stretcher in, and the degree of excitement in his voice as he describes his charge to the desk clerk, are generally more heightened than with the elderly "DOA." One can observe a direct relationship between the loudness and length of the siren alarm and the considered "social value" of the person being transported.

The older the person, the less thorough is the examination he is given; frequently, elderly people are pronounced dead on the basis of only a stethoscopic examination of the heart. The younger the person, the more likely will an examination preceding an announcement of death entail an inspection of the eyes, attempt to find a pulse and touching of the body for coldness. When a younger person is brought to the hospital and while announced by the driver as a "possible" is nonetheless observed to be breathing slightly, or have an audible heart beat, there is a fast mobilization of effort to stimulate increased breathing and a more rapid heart beat. If an older person is brought in in a similar condition there will be a rapid mobilization of similar efforts; however, the time which will elapse between that point at which breathing noticeably ceases and the heart audibly stops beating, and when the pronouncement of death is made, will differ according to his age.

One's location in the age structure of the society is not the only factor which will influence the degree of care he gets when his death is considered to have possibly occurred. At County Hospital a notable additional set of considerations can be generally termed as the patient's presumed "moral character." The detection of alcohol on the breath of a "DOA" is nearly always noticed by the examining physician,

who announces to his fellow workers that the person is a
drunk, and seems to constitute a feature he regards as warranting less than strenuous effort to attempt revival. The
alcoholic patient is treated by hospital physicians, not only
when the status of his body as alive or dead is at stake, but
throughout the whole course of medical treatment, as one
for whom the concern to treat can properly operate somewhat weakly. There is a high proportion of alcoholic patients at County, and their treatment very often involves an
earlier admission of "terminality" and a consequently more
marked suspension of curative treatment than is observed in
the treatment of nonalcoholic patients. In one case, the decision whether or not to administer additional needed blood
to an alcoholic man who was bleeding severely from a stomach ulcer was decided negatively, and that decision was announced as based on the fact of his alcoholism. The intern
in charge of treating the patient was asked by a nurse,
"Should we order more blood for this afternoon?" The doctor answered, "I can't see any sense in pumping it into him
because even if we can stop the bleeding, he'll turn around
and start drinking again and next week he'll be back needing
more blood." In the DOA circumstance, alcoholic patients
have been known to be pronounced dead on the basis of a
stethoscopic examination of the heart alone, even though
that person was of such an age that were he not an alcoholic
he would have likely received much more intensive consideration before being so designated. Among other categories of
persons whose deaths will be more quickly adjudged, and
whose "dying" more readily noticed and used as a rationale
for palliative care, are the suicide, the dope addict, the
known prostitute, the assailant in a crime of violence, the
vagrant, the known wifebeater and other persons whose
moral characters are considered reproachable.

Within a limited temporal perspective at least, but one
which is not necessarily to be regarded as trivial, the likeli-

hood of "dying" and even of being "dead" can thus be said to be partially a function of one's place in the social structure, and not simply in the sense that the wealthier get better care, or at least not in the usual sense of that fact.[2] If one anticipates having a critical heart attack, he best keep himself well-dressed and his breath clean if there is a likelihood he will be brought into the County Emergency Unit as a "possible."

There are a series of practical consequences of publicly announcing that a patient is dead in the hospital setting. His body may be properly stripped of clothing and jewelry, wrapped up for discharge, the family notified of the death and the coroner informed in the case of DOA deaths. In the Emergency Unit there are a special set of procedures which are partially definitive of death. DOA cases are very interestingly "used" in many American hospitals. The inflow of dead bodies, or what can properly be taken to be dead bodies, is regarded as a collection of "guinea pigs," in the sense that a set of procedures can be performed upon those bodies for the sake of teaching and research.

In any "teaching hospital" (in the case of County, I use this term in a weak sense, a hospital which employs interns and residents; in other settings a "teaching hospital" may mean systematic, institutionalized instruction), the environment of medical events is regarded not merely as a collection of treatable cases, but as a collection of experience-relevant information. It is a continually enforced way of looking at the cases one treats under the auspices of a concern for experience with "such cases." This concern can legitimately warrant the institution of a variety of procedures, tests and inquiries which lie outside and may even, on occasion, conflict with the strict interests of treatment; they fall within the interests of learning "medicine," gaining experience with such cases and acquiring technical skills. A principle for organizing medical care activities in the teaching hospital, and perhaps more so in a county hospital where patients' social value is often not highly regarded, is the relevance of any particular activity to the acquisition of skills of general import. Physicians feel that among the greatest values of such institutions is the ease with which they can selectively organize medical attention so as to maximize the benefits to knowledge and technical proficiency which working with a given case expectably afford. The notion of the "interesting case" is, at County, not simply a casual notion, but an enforced principle for the allocation of attention. The private physician is in a more committed relation to each and every one of his patients, and while he may regard this or that case as more or less interesting, he ideally cannot legitimate the interestingness of his patients' conditions as bases for devoting varying amounts of attention to them. His reward for treating the uninteresting case is, of course, the fee, and physicians are known to give more attention to the patients who will be paying more.

At County Hospital, a case's degree of interest is a crucial fact, and one which is invoked to legitimate the way a physician does and should allocate his attention. In surgery I found many examples. If, on a given morning in one operating room a "rare" procedure was scheduled, and in another a "usual" procedure planned, there would be no special difficulty in getting personnel to witness and partake in the "rare" procedure, whereas work in the "usual" case was considered as merely work, regardless of such considerations as the relative fatality rate of each procedure or the patient's physical condition. It is not uncommon to find interns at County interchange among themselves in scrubbing for an appendectomy, each taking turns going next door to watch the skin graft or chest surgery. At Cohen, such house staff interchanging was not permissible. Interns and residents were assigned to a particular surgical suite and required to stay throughout the course of the procedure. On the medical wards, on the basis of general observation, it seems that one could obtain a high order correlation between the amount of time doctors spent discussing and examining patients and the degree of unusualness of their medical problems.

I introduce this general feature to point to the predominant orientation, at County, to such matters as "getting practice," and the general organizational principle which provides for the propriety of using cases as the basis for this practice. Not only are live patients objects of practice, so are dead ones.

There is a rule, in the Emergency Unit, that with every DOA a doctor should attempt to insert an "endotracheal" tube. This should be done only after the patient is pronounced dead. The reason for this practice (and it is a rule on which new interns are instructed as part of their training in doing emergency medicine), is that such a tube is extremely difficult to insert, requiring great yet careful force and, insofar as it causes great pain, cannot be "practiced" on live patients. The body must be positioned with the neck held at an angle that this large tube will go down the proper channel. In some circumstances when it is necessary to establish a rapid "airway" (an open breathing canal), the endotracheal tube can apparently be an effective substitute for the tracheotomy incision. The DOA's body, in its transit from the scene of the death to the morgue constitutes an ideal experimental opportunity. The procedure is not done on all deceased patients, the reason apparently being that it is part of the training one receives on the Emergency Unit, and to be learned there. Nor is it done on all DOA cases, for some doctors, it seems, are uncomfortable in handling a dead body whose charge as a live one they never had, and handling it in the way such a procedure requires. It is important to note that when it is done, it is done most frequently and most intensively with those persons lowly situated in the social structure. No instances were observed where a young child was used as an object for such practice, nor where a well-dressed, middle-aged, middle-class adult was similarly used.

On one occasion a woman, who had seemingly ingested a fatal amount of Clorox, was brought to the Emergency Unit and after her death several physicians took turns trying to insert an endotracheal tube, after which one of them suggested that the stomach be pumped to examine its contents to try to see what effects the Clorox had on the gastric secretions. A lavage was set up and the stomach contents removed. A chief resident left the room and gathered together a group of interns with the explanation that they should look at this woman because of the apparent results of such ingestion. In effect, the doctors conducted their own autopsy investigation without making any incisions.

On several similar occasions, physicians explained that with these cases they didn't really feel like they were prying in handling the body, but that they often did in the case of an ordinary or "natural death" of a morally proper person. Suicidal victims are frequently the object of curiosity, and while among the nursing staff there is a high degree of distaste in working with such patients and their bodies doctors do not express such a high degree of distaste. There was a woman who came into the Emergency Unit with a self-inflicted gunshot wound, which ran from her sternum downward and backward, passing out through a kidney. She had apparently bent over a rifle and pulled the trigger. Upon her "arrival" in the Emergency Unit she was quite alive and talkative, and while in great pain and very fearful, was able to conduct something of a conversation. She was told that she would need immediate surgery, and was taken off to the O.R. She was followed by a group of physicians, all of whom were interested in seeing what damage the path of the bullet had done. One doctor said aloud, quite near her stretcher,

"I can't get my heart into saving her, so we might as well have some fun out of it." During the operation, the doctors regarded her body much as they would during an autopsy. After the critical damage was repaired and they had reason to feel the woman would survive, they engaged in numerous surgical side ventures, exploring muscular tissue in areas of the back through which the bullet had passed but where no damage requiring special repair had to be done, with the exception of tying off bleeders and suturing. One of the operating surgeons performed a side operation, incising an area of skin surrounding the entry wound on the chest, to examine, he announced to colleagues, the structure of the tissue through which the bullet passed. He explicitly announced his project to be motivated by curiosity. One of the physicians spoke of the procedure as an "autopsy on a live patient," about which there was a little laughter.

In another case, a man was wounded in the forehead by a bullet, and after the damage was repaired in the wound, which resembled a natural frontal lobotomy, an exploration was made of an area adjacent to the path of the bullet, on the forehead proper below the hairline. During this exploration the operating surgeon asked a nurse to ask Dr. X to come in. When Dr. X arrived, the two of them, under the gaze of a large group of interns and nurses, made a further incision, which an intern described to me as unnecessary in the treatment of the man, and which left a noticeable scar down the side of the temple. The purpose of this venture was to explore the structure of that part of the face. This area of the skull, that below the hairline, cannot be examined during an autopsy because of a contract between local morticians and the Department of Pathology, designed to leave those areas of the body which will be viewed, free of surgical incisions. The doctors justified the additional incision by pointing out that since he would have a "nice scar as it was, a little bit more wouldn't be so serious."

During autopsies themselves, bodies are routinely used to gain experience in surgical techniques, and many incisions and explorations are conducted that are not essential to the key task of uncovering the cause of the death. On frequent occasions, specialists-in-training came to autopsies having no interest in the patient's death. They would await the completion of the legal part of the procedure, at which point the body is turned over to them for practice. Mock surgical procedures are staged on the body, oftentimes with two co-workers simulating actual conditions, tying off blood vessels which obviously need not be tied or suturing internally.

When a patient died in the Emergency Unit, whether or not he had been brought in under the designation "DOA," there occasionally occurred various mock surgical procedures on his body. In one case a woman was treated for a chicken bone lodged in her throat. Rapidly after her arrival via ambulance a tracheotomy incision was made in the attempt to establish an unobstructed source of air, but the procedure was not successful and she died as the incision was being made. Several interns were called upon to practice their stitching by closing the wound as they would on a live patient. There was a low peak in the activity of the ward, and a chief surgical resident used the occasion to supervisorily teach them various techniques for closing such an incision. In another case the body of a man who died after being crushed by an automobile was employed for instruction and practice in the use of various fracture setting techniques. In still another instance several interns and residents attempted to suture a dead man's dangling finger in place on his mangled hand.

VI

"Babies" and "Mothers"

In this chapter I should like to briefly describe a rather special setting of "death" and "dying" within the hospital, the circumstance of the stillborn and premature "death." To explore some of the especially troublesome problems in this area, several months were spent witnessing deliveries and ward procedures in the maternity section of County. This setting of "death" is sufficiently different, in its ideological and organizational features, from the rest of County Hospital, to warrant special, if only limited, attention.

At County Hospital, there is a system of definitions and weights intended to describe the status of fetuses. According to its weight, length and period of gestation, at the end of which it is delivered or "expelled," a fetus is either considered "human" or not. At County, the dividing line is 550 grams, 20 centimeters and 20 weeks of gestation. Any creature having smaller dimensions or of lesser embryonic "age" is considered nonhuman. A term sometimes used to describe such a "thing" is an "aborted fetus," or simply "abortus." If "born" without signs of life, it is placed in a jar for pathological examination, properly flushed down the toilet or otherwise simply disposed of. Any creature having larger dimensions or greater embryonic "age" is considered human, and if "born" without signs of life, or if born with signs of life which cease to be noticeable at some later point, cannot be permissibly flushed down the toilet, but must be accorded a proper ritual departure from the human race. Not only must it be properly departed, it must, as a condition for being departed, be first admitted. I am talking here of a "thing" which, at the minimum level of acceptability, would be about the size of a pound of butter. This "human" must be admitted to the hospital, wrapped in a morgue sheet, placed in the hospital morgue and buried in the ground by an authorized burier. Creatures under the definitional limit are not considered to be "dead," for to be "dead," where being "dead" consists of that status which requires a variety of Death Procedures, one must first be capable of being seen as one which at least could have been alive. "Life," in turn, is not simply the biological phenomenon of cellular activity, but a socially constituted state of affairs. A "thing" which makes the limit, will have its existence duly recorded in the official tallies of the society, from the hospital's yearly demographic inventory to the United States Census Reports.

A fetus of fifteen weeks' gestation, weighing less than one pound, shorter than six inches and which pulsates, for example, is nonetheless not a live human, for a live human is procedurally defined as a creature which is to be admitted to the hospital and can die, be treated as a dead person, be given a burial. A pulsating nonhuman will not be disposed of, nor will it be admitted to the hospital; its status will be that simply of a "thing," and once it stops pulsating, which almost universally occurs after its expulsion from the womb and detachment from the placenta, it will be disposed of. It does not move from life to death, as these categories are socially used, but from biological activity to inactivity. No attempts will be made to keep it pulsating, despite the fact that some doctors agree that biological activity can be artificially stimulated and thereby sustained for an extended period of time. A pediatrician explained that a fetus of some 18 or 20 weeks' gestation could be kept alive for some time if placed in an incubator and fed artificially. He noted that this has been achieved on an experimental basis. Whether feasible, possible or impossible, so far as I could tell such efforts were not made. These "things" are considered nonviable.

The fetus which passes the definitional limit and is considered a "human," dead or alive, is, however, not always treated as the regulations require. The 20 week gestated fetus, exceeding 20 centimeters and 550 grams is, if pulsating at birth, ideally to be placed in an incubator and treated as a hospital patient. In over 95 percent of the cases, a fetus of that size will not survive more than hours or days after birth, even when incubated, given the current state of medical skill in these areas and, perhaps, the medical concern to develop them. The survival rate increases in a clear, straight, linear progression with increased weight and gestation and this relationship may be partially a function of the kind of care given fetuses of different sizes. If the fetus is a borderline case, staff members will generally not put it in an incubator, but rather, by keeping it in open air, allow it to "die" very shortly after its delivery. Should the fetus cry, however, or take what is regarded as a breath, it will be incubated, the cry or sound seemingly taken to represent a more developed embryo. Once sounds are uttered, regarding its status as a "thing" seems to be hard to do. At Cohen Hospital, a similar practice exists. If the "baby" takes a breath or cries, that fact is taken to constitute evidence of its humanness and warrants regarding its possible life or possible death as the lives and deaths of other humans are normally regarded. A difference at Cohen is that burials are

not required unless the family requests them, even for a
full-term stillborn child, while at County proper burials are
required for a definitionally adequate "human" that gets
recorded as such. The fact of "crying" or "breathing" is of
social significance, it seems, because, as best as can be gathered from discussions I had with medical personnel, these
occurrences in themselves have no special medical significance. The 20 week gestated fetus which cries is in no better
shape, medically speaking, than a similarly aged one which
is "silent" ("silent" is perhaps not an appropriate term, for
to be "silent" one must presumably be capable of "silenc-
ing"). "Crying" or "breathing" seem to be socially significant, as "cries for help" as it were.

Delivery room staff have some latitude in assigning the
statuses of life, death, human or "abortus", as such deter-
minations are not always precisely made with the use of a
scale. The decision in any given case rests upon whether
medical and nursing personnel assess the "thing's" life
chances as good or poor, and upon what they assess as the
consequences of assigning status for other activities, which
shall be discussed later. While weight, length and "age" are
generally employed as rough guides, the exhibition of "human behavior" in the form of a cry or breath can operate to
provide the "thing," which is legally under the limit, with
the status of a "human" and the absence of such "behavior"
is often taken to legitimate treating an otherwise legal "human" as an "abortus," particularly if its dimensions barely
exceed borderline requirements.

While some flexibility is permissible in assigning these
statuses, there is always care exercised in attempting to treat
that which might be properly considered a "human" by dis-
posal. This care is warranted by the fact that certain patients are known to get overly sensitive about their "products" and to complain later that what they regarded as
"their baby" was treated as a specimen. Catholic patients

are notably regarded as troublesome in this respect, and
Catholic staff members are characteristically more conserva-
tive in their use of the definitional criteria. Some of the
Catholic staff members claim that the criteria are too high.
On several known occasions Catholic "parents" issued complaints afterwards when they learned that "their baby" was
disposed of, and on various instances at County a Catholic
intern or resident required a duly recorded entry and dismissal of a "thing" which other delivery room staff would
have preferred to treat as a specimen. There is the general
feeling among the Protestant members of the delivery room
staff that the legal definitions are too strict and too low, and
that the procedures of wrapping, discharging and burying a
one pound fetus border on obscenity. Once a death certificate is made out, the procedures of discharge, wrapping and
burial must be carried out, and the doctor has the final decision in whether or not to prepare such a certificate. One
Catholic intern got a relatively bad name for himself in the
delivery room by preparing such certificates for almost all
deliveries of nonviable creatures, and despite attempts by
other interns, residents, and nurses to "reason with him,"
he insisted upon his right to make such decisions.

The circumstances of a delivery are especially interesting
from the standpoint of the relative's awareness of the death.
Here, unlike other circumstances at County, the relative is
immediately present at the scene of "death," and this scene
is particularly susceptible to rather tense moments. Women
in our society (and perhaps everywhere in the world) expect their newly delivered infants to cry aloud rather shortly
after delivery, and indeed they normally do. The longer the
amount of time between the complete expulsion of the infant
from the womb and the point where crying begins, the more
tense the interactional situation becomes. The practice at
County is to immediately put the "mother" to sleep when a
biologically troublesome infant is delivered. Modern gas

anesthetics allow for a very rapid induction of sleep so that
at that point when physicians feel crying will never come,
or feel that the time passage has gotten obviously too extended, they give a well-understood, visual order to the attending nurse or anesthetist to administer gas. Women are
often kept considerably doped up during the final moments
of their deliveries, and one obstetrician reported that this
is as much to be able to quickly put them under if trouble
occurs as for their pain during the delivery. Obstetricians
employ an interesting device to handle the perpetually possible situation of trouble. As soon as the baby's head appears
at the opening of the vagina, they obtain a suctioning
syringe. When the head itself comes out sufficiently far so
that the mouth can be entered, the doctor starts to suction
mucous and stimulate crying. The reason for this practice,
over and above the concern to quickly get the infant on "outside air," is that the sooner the doctor attempts to stimulate
crying, the sooner he will be able to detect trouble and have
ample time to order anesthesia before the mother becomes
aware of any difficulty. Mothers expect to hear crying once
they have delivered the entire baby, which they can apparently feel. Starting suctioning early thus gives the doctor a
safety margin regarding the simultaneous detection of trouble; the arrangements whereby the mother cannot witness
what goes on "down-under" from her position, aides in giving the doctor leeway. Obstetricians complained, at County,
about the new practice whereby a mirror is placed such that
women can witness the delivery of the child. This mirror
allows the mother more scrutiny over the critical area and
its happenings than some doctors prefer them to have.

Should the mother detect trouble, which seems to infrequently occur, she is vaguely and evasively told not to worry,
and gas is quickly given, usually with an explanation to the
mother that gas must be given before suturing the episiot-
omy. In several known instances "mothers" were observed

to cry out such things as "My baby is dead, isn't it?" Doctors at County do not attend this as a question, but instead respond with something like, "Relax, Mrs. ———" (or, at County, often, Miss) and gas is quickly administered.

The most frequent occasion of the delivery of a "dead" fetus is the premature delivery, and the more premature the delivery is, the more the mother expects a nonviable being to be expelled. It is with the unexpected stillborn delivery that interactional problems are most severe, though even here, very few instances at County were observed where anesthetics were insufficient to manage at least temporarily the task of separating the relative from the scene of the "death."

Doctors and nurses use, as indications of the mother's attachment to the "child-to-be," the manner of her behavior in those critical moments of silence, and throughout the course of her delivery. At County, there is the general feeling that a great proportion of the newborns are "unwanted," and this is said to be substantiated by the fact that premature deliveries and deliveries of stillborns are not only taken coolly, but are often occasions for the expression of relief. On three known occasions, women were heard to express joy with the delivery of a nonviable "infant." The more indifferent the mother's attitude toward the entire process of childbirth and in that period of tense silence which attends the delivery of a "baby-in-trouble," the more comfortable staff members feel about treating a borderline case as nonhuman. The woman who throughout the course of her delivery, moans that she doesn't want the baby is regarded as one who will be least upset if a barely adequate, "legal human" is later treated as a specimen.

In the greatest proportion of cases, despite the slight degree of latitude delivery room personnel have in making such decisions, the outcome of distributions into the various status categories corresponds closely to the weight, length and age criteria. The consequences of treating a one pound, six inch, "thing," as a "human" are worthy of some comment, for a special set of administrative problems surround the handling of these "things," regarding the responsibility of having a burial, and the social organization of the hospital morgue.

These special consequences of "death" provide that category with some additionally interesting social features. Such "things" are wrapped up and placed in the hospital morgue, and the "parents" are informed that it is their responsibility to contact a funeral parlor to arrange for a burial for their "child." A very common happening at County, one which staff members characteristically point to as prototypical of the general "immorality" of the patient population, is that such "babies" are very frequently deserted in the morgue; no funeral parlor is contacted, and after a period of days, weeks, and in some cases months, the "baby's" remains remain in the morgue. Many such "parents" are hard to reach, for many of them give incorrect names on their admission to the hospital, particularly the unmarried "mothers."

The county has a service which it provides for the relatives of families who cannot afford a funeral service and who can provide evidence of this financial inability. The hospital employs a "funeral director," has a very old hearse which it uses to transport deceased patients from the hospital to the county cemetery, and in the basement of the hospital, devotes a large section of the carpentry department to the manufacture of caskets, a practice which seems nonexistent in noncharity hospitals in the United States. If the relatives desire, and make adequate arrangements in advance, a simple graveside ceremony can be conducted. Very few of County's deceased patients' families are able to demonstrate their eligibility for this service, because the hospital maintains a list of private funeral establishments which offer reduced rates for charity patients, and these rates are sometimes very low. The hospital "eligibility workers," in charge of screening families in this respect, have a rule that if any private establishment's services can be afforded, as they assess what persons can afford, the county burial will be refused. An eligibility worker reported that there are few requests made for such services, that most families want to give their deceased relatives private funerals and that many of the families have funeral insurance and family plots. The same is not true as regards stillborns and "premies."

The same requirement for demonstrating financial inability operates to obtain a county burial for a "deceased stillborn," or "deceased premie." The parents must come into the hospital, with an appointment to "see an eligibility worker" (the phrasing of the admitting nurse who often spends half her day telephoning families to inform them of this responsibility:), and arrange to have the county bury their "child." It is interesting that the terms "child" and "baby" are used to refer to these objects, while those below the limit are never referred to as such. The admitting nurse uses, as one device to get families to come in for interviews, a form letter which she sends three times, after which the police are notified of the case. The letter begins: "Dear ———, this letter is regarding the burial of your baby, born ———."

A major effort is required to keep the morgue relatively free of a large backlog of piled up, wrapped "fetuses." At any given time in the morgue there are usually some twenty such packages, as compared with the usual morgue census of half a dozen adult bodies, although the death rate is higher among adults. On repeated occasions, the number became so excessive that morgue personnel became rather desperate, in part because of the terrible stench that was created which the pathologist claimed kept doctors from attending autopsies, and in part because needed space was taken up by these "things." When such a situation occurred, pressure was exerted upon the eligibility staff to authorize county burials, despite the lack of formal interviews with families. The concern to keep the turnover rate high occasionally operated to legitimate a more lenient attitude toward financial responsibility, so that if a "parent" simply came into the hospital and said he could not afford a private burial, the OK was given. Periodically, a vigorous campaign to dispose of the backlog was instituted, and the admitting nurse spent several days on the telephone trying to contact as many "parents" as was possible. Once a rule was established that if a "baby" stayed in the morgue for more than six weeks, it could be buried without a financial interview, and a large batch of "babies" was thereby carried out. Usually, the casket makers in the basement prepare special little boxes for these burials, but on this occasion, much to the later dismay of the hospital administrator, all were placed in a single adult coffin, whereupon the six-week rule was abolished.

The entire situation is regarded by many people at County as rather obnoxious. The requirement for a burial, uncommon at other hospitals where that matter is up to the family to decide, is accredited to the fact of the Catholic District Attorney's peculiar interest and personal influence as regards such matters. "Death" and "dying" become particularly interesting in this area, where a "thing," by virtue of a system of numerical definitions, can become the discussed, responsible object of a variety of administrative officials, and a cumbersome bureaucratic set of procedures established by virtue of a difference in ounces of flesh. If a fetus makes a cry or takes a breath it thereby establishes its right to treatment within some of the ordinary economic, administrative, ritual and familial institutions of the welfare and civil society. Its social existence can be established if it grows, prenatally, to an adequate size. Form letters speaking of it as a "baby," the manufacture of miniature caskets, the requirement for fulfilling "parental" responsibilities toward it, its entry into the official demographic records via the required birth and death certificates are among the treatments which make such an object a social one. They can be said to constitute a minimal definition of life and death. There is a beginning and an end, and nothing much in between but perhaps a heartbeat or two, yet that beginning and end are marked by the standardized, obligatory, societal formats by which all beginnings and ends are attended.

Perhaps one of the reasons County has such difficulty in having "parents" assume their "responsibilities" toward their deceased offspring is that the notion of a "parent" is not mutually shared by eligibility staff and these men and women, not that these people are "irresponsible." The enforcement of a responsibility to bury one's kin would seem to operate only if the respect for the deceased person as "kin" is operative. In the delivery room, women are often addressed as "mother," even though they may have no children, and oftentimes before the infants they are expected to deliver are actually delivered. Obstetricians at both County and Cohen characteristically conversed with their patients before and during the delivery, and used the term "mother" in directing comments to them, giving advice, instructions, asking for their sensations. This usage is generally not employed until the woman actually comes into the delivery room and begins to "crown," when the baby's head appears at the opening of the vagina, though the head itself has not actually begun to pass through. This appearance is taken to warrant such talk as "Come on now, mother, you're doing fine, take a deep breath," or "A little while more, mother, and it will be here," or "His head is coming through, mother, one more good push and it will be all over." A woman who is five months pregnant and therefore considered about to be delivering a nonviable "thing," will not be so referred to in the delivery room, even if she is actually a mother by virtue of the children she has at home. The use of the term "mother" is rather special here, referring as it does, not to a formally constituted kinship category, but to "mothering," conceived as the activity of producing what is likely to be a live, human child. Caution is used in employing the term the shorter the length of the woman's pregnancy, typically being restricted only to those women who are at full-term. Should a woman at full-term be referred to as "mother" and then deliver a stillborn infant, all further references to her as "mother" are thereupon suspended.

It is a matter outside the scope of the present chapter to consider the special properties of "motherhood" under varying conditions, such as when an older child dies and is an only child, do "parents" retain their claims to be so referred to? Can a woman properly consider herself a "mother" even though she has no other children other than the one who was born a stillborn? In the County case, given the use of "mother" in this special, pre-birth, perhaps preparatory way, we can have the circumstance of a woman being a "mother," in the sense of being entitled to be so referred to, even though she has never had children, and was properly so called only during that period of time between the beginning of her delivery and the birth of a stillborn. Yet at the same time, she is expected to abide by "family responsibilities" in arranging a funeral for "her child."

VII

"Bad News"

There are certain hospital events of such a status that it is considered necessary to report them to members of a patient's family, whether or not inquiry is made about them. A sudden turn for the worse, the outcome of a surgical procedure, the result of a child delivery, the findings of a laboratory investigation of expected import and the occurrence of a death are among such "announceable events." [1]

There are rules regarding those personnel who are to be responsible for reporting such events and those who are specifically prohibited from doing so. At County, the responsibility is with the physicians; at Cohen, it is limited to the physician-in-charge-of-the-case. Should inquiry be made concerning an announceable event to a member of the staff with no authority to announce such events, the inquirer is referred to a proper person. Should a relative at County inquire of a nurse, "what did the test show?" he is to be referred to a physician. Should a relative ask a Cohen nurse the same question, he must be referred to the patient's private physician.

Most announceable events in the hospital are generated

in specifically structured episodic ways. Persons await the outcome of a surgical procedure, of laboratory investigations known to be in progress, expectant fathers await the births of their children. Awaiting news of these events occurs within clearly framed outcome situations, with a well-defined expectation on the part of awaiting members. It is an important fact about deaths, however, that they do not usually occur as the outcomes of such episodes, but rather, they take place in the course of downwardly progressing illnesses. An exception of sorts is the DOA case, where relatives are called to the hospital, typically with little information as to what has transpired, and arrive very much attuned to the scene as a news-producing one.

Very seldom does it occur that members of a patient's family are in a situation where they await the news of the patient's progress with respect to life and death as they do such matters as surgical outcomes. In episodically structured situations, for example in surgery or the delivery room circumstance, a special degree of forthrightness is required in the manner of an announcer. If the recipient of the news can regard the appearance of an announcer on the scene as motivated by the news he brings, then a "right to know" is immediately enforceable, with the degree of urgency and solemnity apparently commensurate with the presumed severity of the matter about to be announced. In announcing the outcomes of such procedures, announcers feel obliged to avoid circuitous routes to the news. It would be felt highly improper for the physician announcing the sex and condition of a newborn to an awaiting father, to do so by first initiating a conversation and, over the course of that conversation, gradually releasing the awaited information. Many matters which physicians know are told to family members with considerations of tact, embarrassment, the emotional readiness of the recipient and whether or not it is the place of the one who has the information to tell the other. When, however, there is a clear expectation that news is forthcoming, such considerations are more difficult to sustain. It would be considered improper for a physician to withhold news of an operation's outcome because he feels that it might displease the recipient, or to delay news of the newborn because the parent had hoped for the opposite sex.[2] The obligation to directly report such matters, once face-to-face contact is initiated, is at least partially due to the fact that the announcement is considered to be of some import and that the recipient is taken to be highly keyed up to hearing some news.

Should staff members wish, for whatever reasons, to avoid telling the waiting relative some news in such circumstances, their main strategy is to avoid contact with him. The more such occasions are structured as episodes, with clear beginnings and ends, the more difficult it is for an announcer to appear before relatives without news. Surgeons, for example, carefully arrange their rounds in the hospital so that once they go into surgery, they will emerge from behind the scrutinized doors only when they carry the news being awaited. Once the surgeon has been behind the doors for some time, he must stay back there until ready for his final emergence. Only the first few minutes or so have enough degree of freedom that should he reappear, the assumption is that things "haven't yet begun."

In such clear episode-like situations, persons with no authority to relate news both create and rely upon the fiction that the critical event's occurrence almost coincides with the appearance of the proper announcer, that until he appears there is nothing to relate. Typically there is, in these situations, a clear distinction between the "frontstage" & "backstage" areas, and persons with no authority to announce events can emerge from backstage areas and nonetheless act vis-a-vis the recipient-to-be as though the event whose reporting they await has not yet taken place. While staff members who walked back and forth across the public waiting room as they entered and left the surgical area at Cohen often found that eyes jumped to them every time they appeared, they felt they could rely on the knowledge waiters had of the authority structure.

Waiters for news do not have accurate knowledge of the goings on in backstage areas, not knowing whether or not a particular person appearing from behind the doors was involved in their relative's case. So long as a variety of activities are taken to go on behind the doors, particular personnel cannot be matched with particular cases, unless waiters have personal knowledge of those persons who are attending their relatives. The backstage area is perceived by members of the public as consisting of a complex maze of independent subareas. In such situations, where news of import is expected, one can observe announcers to give signs very rapidly as to what recipients are to expect. Should the surgery's outcome be poor, surgeons, as they appear from behind the doors to the operating suites, often assume a decidedly solemn appearance, giving indication to awaiting relatives that the news they bring is unfavorable. Such preparation seeks to effectively place recipients in a subdued frame of mind, so that they don't rush up to the surgeon with anxious questions, making it more difficult for him to deliver the bad news, but in anticipation of it, remain silently poised to hear the worst. In instances where news is favorable, announcers are known to quickly indicate that fact in their approach to recipients. They walk very quickly towards them, attempting to shorten the amount of time when the recipient will be unduly worried. Surgeons have been observed to leave the operating room with broad smiles on their faces, and begin talking long before they get within usual conversational distance.

Physicians use the physical layout and perceived expected lengths of procedure in a variety of ways. In the surgical setting, surgeons were observed to finish the critical parts of an operation, turn the sewing-up tasks over to residents and interns, and then take an extended break before having to greet relatives. In one instance, a surgeon was observed to remove his cap, mask and cloth shoecovers as he adjourned from the operating room proper to the doctor's lounge and then, after chatting for a half hour with his colleagues, put his cap and mask back on, with the mask hanging around his neck in that position which suggests it was just taken off. He then left the area and talked with the family. With the cap and mask on, he reported afterwards, it appears as though he has just put down the needle and suturing thread and carries exceedingly fresh news. There is apparently always some danger that with such delays the physician will forget about his task. At County, an intern spent a long time talking with a student nurse after he had delivered a baby, and when he left the delivery area to return to his sleeping room, he nearly forgot the relative, almost passing him in the hall before he realized his obligation.

In situations where there is a clear expectation of news to come, staff members rely upon the definition of such situations as tense ones to provide for a necessary degree of anxiousness on the part of awaiting relatives. This tenseness operates to minimize the likelihood that relatives will behave with an inappropriate degree of nonchalance in face of possible bad news. In the case of deaths, which seldom occur within such time-specific, either-or contexts, unless staff effort is quickly taken in the handling of an uninformed relative, there is the likelihood that sufficient self-control will not be exercised and that the unknowledgeable bereaved person will act as though nothing of special import had happened. Those members of the staff who are not permitted to announce deaths find themselves in the uncomfortable psychological situation of witnessing a person whom they know is now a bereaved but who is not himself aware of his new status.

The requirements for a redefinition of the situation most acutely occur should the relative engage the staff members in casual conversation, which is more likely the more extended the patient's stay had been and the more acquainted the relative is with members of the staff. Nurses experience considerable strain when a relative with whom they are well-acquainted greets them in the hall in cheerful tones. The fact that the conditions for his cheerfulness have been altered by an event whose occurrence is not known or anticipated by the bereaved-to-be makes staff members feel deceitful should they allow interaction to proceed with him "as usual." Improper personnel, those not permitted to make announcements, have difficulty in such situations. They feel that the bereaved has an immediate right to learn of his bereavement, or, at least, the right to know that a serious matter has occurred, of which he will be shortly informed. The attempt is made to place a new frame around events, to rapidly give the situation an outcome structure, make it an episode and quickly cut off whatever interaction might develop which would be inadvertently based on the bereaved's ignorance of his own circumstance. Nurses have been observed to rapidly approach an unknowledgeable bereaved-to-be as they see him appear within sight, so as to shorten the period of time when the bereaved would be naïvely entering a situation which, were he aware of its character, would be approached with cautiousness and preparedness.[3]

When a death occurs, direct announcement, with no circuity or delay, is enforceable without respect for whether or not the family anticipates its likelihood. The enforceable character of a prompt, straightforward announcement of death derives less from the structure of an occasion than from the strongly held sentiment that persons have a right to an immediate informing of their own status as newly bereaved. A laboratory test which indicates the presence of an incurable disease will be felt to be an announceable matter. Unless, however, the family is expected to be awaiting such an announcement and they view a physician's particular encounter with them as generated by the news of the outcome, the physician may release such news with considerably less urgency, framing it so as to sensitively attend the relative's fears and expectations. When a death occurs, staff members feel the unknowledgeable bereaved has a right to an urgent telling, and with every moment which passes in which the unknowledgeable bereaved remains ignorant, no matter how effectively the situation has been given episodic features and the relative is made aware that something of great moment has occurred, staff feel more uneasy in having him around. Nurses, not properly able to announce deaths, have been observed to leave the scene of such an awaiting bereaved-to-be because they could not retain their own composure. This was the case most noticeably on the pediatrics ward, when a young child had died, and, generally, seemed most acutely bothersome where, for whatsoever reasons, staff members found themselves saddened by the death and sympathetic toward the bereaved.

A set of resources generally available in nondeath circumstances cannot be used here. Personnel cannot advise the family not to worry, nor do they feel up to engaging in niceties, exchanging smiles or otherwise doing those things which they might to help the recipient fill the time until the proper announcer arrives. In the surgery situation, nurses in the station adjacent to the waiting room had the task of acting as objects of tension reduction by conducting passing talk with anxious waiters. When a death occurred, however, staff members felt that to say anything whatever was unkind, as it risked invitation to discourse which, they felt, the bereaved-to-be would not wish to engage in were he to know the details of his circumstances. While in the episodically structured situation the fiction that no news exists prior to the doctor's appearance allows staff to make conversation, when they know of a death's occurrence a qualitatively different attitude in their regard for a recipient-to-be prevails. The whole class of comforting remarks and gestures, otherwise appropriate, are, with death, considered radically inappropriate. Until death, staff members have available, as devices for offering comfort, the use of qualifications on the actual seriousness of the occurrence. For cancers, it is proposed that there is always the hope of X-ray therapy, and further surgery, for "sudden turns for the worse" there is always the chance that he will "pull through." Every announcement in the hospital, save that of a death, can properly have qualificatory remarks appended to it, devised to reduce its apparent seriousness or at least offer some form of "hope."

While in some Cohen circumstances news of a death was "broken gently," in most of the announcements of death I observed that was not done. In the DOA cases on which my observations of death announcements were made, physicians felt obliged to deliver news of a death immediately. "Breaking news gently" as an act of comforting, seemed proper only for those who had some degree of intimacy with the recipient, or, as for example in the case of clergymen, some extended role in the postannouncement reaction of the bereaved. The hospital physician has few appropriate resources in such situations and has his task essentially circumscribed as the delivery of the news alone. In the County situation, deaths were felt to require immediate informing and when a proper announcer was not available, attempts were made to isolate the unknowledgeable bereaved as quickly as possible, as much to minimize the emotional pressures felt by the staff as to give privacy to the scene to follow. The relative is escorted to a private room, if one is available, and told to await the doctor's arrival. This is done to guarantee that he will not unwittingly engage others in interaction or be unwittingly so engaged by others, whether those others know of the death but are not permitted to announce such matters (nurses, aides, clerks, administrative personnel) or are unaware that the bereaved-to-be is such.

An additional warrant for isolating such persons, at County particularly, derives from the character of ward social structure. Information about recently occurring deaths is not always transmitted to all personnel in secrecy, as I have pointed out above, so there always exists the possibility that the occurrence of a death will be learned of by one staff member in his conversation with another, and such conversation is not always discreetly conducted in private areas. In one instance, a morgue attendant was observed to arrive at the nurses' desk to secure a deceased patient's belongings and address the nurse, asking where the patient's things were, while the waiting relative was standing alongside the nurses' station awaiting the physician. The nurse managed, by eye signal, to alert the attendant to the bystander's identity and inhibit further references to his relative's body. This sort of possibility is maximized when the news of a death spreads within the hospital, to those occupationally involved in such matters, faster than it spreads to kin, a situation particularly prevalent in County. The fact that bodies are wrapped before their dismissal from the ward bed, presumably a practice which is sanitarily motivated, seems at least possibly due, as well, to the fact that there are never complete safeguards but that a relative of the deceased patient whose body is being brought down the hall might otherwise directly identify his relative.

Several special safeguards are employed to minimize the likelihood of indirect discoveries and improper conversational developments. One practice of wide use is to organize the arrival of the relative so that it will be clearly expected and proper preparations can be taken in advance. This is typically the practice at Cohen Hospital where it is felt more advisable for members of the family to be informed of the death in person. Frequently, a nurse calls the family and informs them that the "patient has taken a turn for the worse and the doctor advises you to come to the hospital." An alternative procedure, occasionally employed at Cohen, is for the nurse to call the family and advise them that the "doctor said he wanted to talk with you and wanted to know where you could be reached." This is done when nurses cannot locate the private physician and want to be able to keep tabs on the relatives' whereabouts. From the standpoint of the hospital, the most easily managed deaths, those requiring the least amount of scrutiny of arriving members of the public, are those which occur at late evening hours. From the physician's standpoint, given his required attention to such events and inability to delegate their care to others, nighttime deaths are inconvenient insofar as he is awakened and must see the family, but more convenient than the daytime death which ties him up at the hospital or on the telephone awaiting the chance to contact members of the family.

Another practice is for nurses, on their own initiative, to call the physician to inform him of the death and then inform families of the need to come to the hospital. They try to insure that the physician will have control over the family's whereabouts and avoid the circumstance where, once the physician arrives, the family might not be capable of being reached, or might unexpectedly and unknowledgeably arrive at the hospital before the physician. Timing is an important consideration: nurses learn from doctors when the latter plan to arrive at the hospital, and time their calls to the families so that family members will expectably arrive after the physician does.

THE ANNOUNCEMENT OF DEATH—
CONVERSATIONAL METHODS FOR THE
HANDLING OF GRIEF

The announcement of death occasions which I shall now examine in detail were mainly those generated by the DOA circumstance at County Hospital. They involved as their participants a family member whose relative had just died, who was not a hospital patient, and an intern or resident on duty in County's Emergency Unit who had no prior acquaintanceship with the family or the deceased before death. Of the fifty-two DOA death announcements I witnessed, thirty-four were the deaths of white persons and eighteen of Negroes. Forty-one cases involved persons over fifty years of age, seven were people between eighteen and forty-two, and six were children. From information gathered by the coroner, who has the responsibility for legal identification and medical investigation of deaths when they occur outside the hospital, or within twenty-four hours after hospital admission, of the thirty-one cases with available occupational histories, six were professional people, fifteen white-collar workers and small businessmen, seven skilled laborers and three unskilled workers. As the Emergency Unit serves as a general facility for ambulance cases of an "emergency" character, and is not restricted to persons with limited incomes, the social class characteristics of DOA persons are considerably more various, and generally more middle class, than those of the hospital's general patient population. On occasion a DOA case is attended by a private physician who has been called to the hospital, and it is he who announces the death to the family. My observations are based entirely on cases where a staff doctor made the announcement.

The occasion of the announcement is typically generated in the following way: a member of the family arrives at the Emergency Unit shortly after the ambulance's arrival, having been told to come to the Unit by policemen or ambulance drivers. In many instances the family member was called from work, in others he was present at the scene of the ambulance pickup, perhaps responsible for notification of the police or ambulance service himself. In these latter circumstances, he might be in a position to directly know, in detail, what it is that has transpired. When not present at the scene but telephoned or otherwise informed to come to the hospital, his expectations as to what to expect may not be clearly formulated. He may have received, by way of notification, the instruction, "Your wife has been in an accident and has been taken to County Hospital," or the notification might have included any other variant degree of information. When he arrives at the hospital, his expectation is more or less formulated depending upon his own witness to the accident event, his knowledge of the person's prior health, the information he has been provided by drivers and police, or other sources. While the fact of having been called into the hospital clearly delimits the range of expectable happenings, what the alternatives are may be unclear.

Physicians feel that incoming relatives, whether or not they know that a death has occurred or have some expectation of such a possibility, must be informed of the death. The physician does not consider it is warranted to not tell the family because the recipient-to-be appears to "already know." There is the strongly felt obligation that as quickly upon his arrival in the hospital as is possible, the relative will be escorted to a private room and the death's occurrence be announced. (It is to be noted that this was the only occurrence at County Hospital, a death, in which a private room was used for conversation between staff members and patients' families.)

Despite the lack of any actual medical intervention in the usual DOA case, hospital personnel are always sensitive to the possible responses of relatives to the institutionalized

definition of the setting and their possible claims that its per-
formers have some rightful responsibility for such matters
as the occurrence of deaths. By sheer virtue of his location
in the social structure, as well as the hospital's, the physician
experiences the obligation to behave with some degree of
accountability for the occurrence of an event beyond his
jurisdiction, involving a set of persons with whom no contractual duties had been undertaken, and a corpse whose
previous breathing, generally speaking, was never witnessed.
By the fact of a death somewhere in the neighboring streets
or residences, and the corpse's delivery to his station, he
must, at least for a short while, assume the status of a committed, involved party. This *de facto* implication is, of
course, one notorious aspect in which the physician's tasks in
delivering bad news differs from those other bearers of sad
tidings, such as the telegraph delivery boy and somewhat less
distinctly, the policeman. While the physician can and does
avoid street accident scenes, the hospital's definition as a
public place and the intern or resident's employment in it,
brings the street inside. As a physician, he cannot, like the
telegram deliverer, merely present the news and leave the
scene, but must evidence some degree of general concern and
responsibility.

The general procedure is for the clerk at the admissions
desk to rapidly escort the family member to a small office,
immediately opposite the entrance way, instruct him to await
the arrival of the doctor and close the door behind him. Personnel at this station, usually a clerk and a nurse, attend the
impending arrival of the DOA's relatives and seek to quickly
locate them once they arrive. It is generally the case that
family members in such situations announce their identities
immediately upon their arrival, their concern being that
news be rapidly obtained, and that staff members be able to
locate them when they have the news. The anxiousness they
evidence serves to place personnel on guard in their presence,

a caution which would be more difficult to exercise and more disruptive of work routines, were relatives to nonchalantly arrive on the scene. This caution is of particularly great importance when the person whose death has been pronounced is not readily identifiable, for example when he carries no wallet identification. Here the sheer fact of a relative's name provides no basis for matching deceased and bereaved. Generally, given the history of events in the Unit, the clerk expects that following the occurrence of a DOA, there will arrive a person who appears particularly anxious. If a name is available for the dead person, with the announcement by the relative of his name the match is made. It is common for relatives to announce, in addition to their names, their relation to the person about whom information they seek and, furthermore, some piece of information about the generation of the event which will additionally serve to match the two parties. "I'm Mr. S., I was told to come here because they brought my son in." "Did they just bring in an elderly woman? I'm her daughter."

It is of interest that no errors were ever made, nor were any reported by staff members, in the matching of deceased to relative, and that this alignment occurs without any visual body identification procedure of the sort which occurs when bodies are in the custody of the police or coroner. The mere announcement of a name, or in several cases where no identification was available on the deceased no more than a remark such as "I was told to come about my father," was regarded as a sufficient basis for assuming that the match had been correctly established, whereupon announcement of the death was made. No additional attempt was made in any case prior to the announcement to specifically insure that the death which the physician was to announce was the death of a party about whom the relative in question sought information.[4]

It is an extremely interesting fact about death, one which

I cannot fully explore here, that persons generally have complete and absolute trust that the procedures of identifying the body and the pronouncement of death have been correctly undertaken. There is apparently complete confidence that those social arrangements which produced the news are without defects, that the person who arrives at the hospital claiming that his father was brought there is, in fact, the son of the man who was brought there and pronounced dead; that the dissemination of news from the ambulance driver, to the policeman, to the wife at home, which results in her coming to the hospital, was errorless; that the physician who read, from the identification card in the wallet, a man's name and telephoned the wife of that man, did not make a mistaken reading.

This confidence in the correctness of procedures is best seen in the announcement scene itself, when the news of the death is delivered. Once the occurrence of the death was announced by the physician, the recipient of the news did not attempt to question, deny, revise, undermine or protest the physician's assertion. Once the death's happening was reported, none of the interchange which followed contested the validity of the purported fact. Rather, what followed in the way of crying, sobbing, moaning and then talking seemed based upon the unquestioned, commonly agreed-upon status of the event being cried, sobbed, moaned and talked about.[5]

Once said, the announcement of the death stood as a permanently correct assertion which needed no documentation or explanation to convince the relative of its actual occurrence. With the doctor's opening words, bereavement occurred. In no instances did relatives voice concern that perhaps an error in identification had been made or that perhaps the pronouncement of death was not accurately conducted. If we consider the available and commonly used procedures for demanding to see evidence, seeking consultation from others, and obtaining proper credentials from a reporter of

news in other circumstances we are struck by the absence of
such questioning here. People regularly use, in medical and
nonmedical settings, their knowledge of the bureaucratically
organized conditions of work for circumventing and doubt-
ing assertions of policy and fact, yet in no announcement of
death occasion was it asked, "Have you enough knowledge
to make such assessments"? or "Let me talk to your su-
perior about this." Claims as to the professional competence
of a reporter of news or witness of affairs, as well as his
personal motives and interests, are routinely made to dis-
credit or evaluate the events he purports to correctly report.
This regularly occurs in the legal system, in the treatment
of medical diagnoses of serious illnesses where consultation
is sought from others.

Death seems to be a perfect example of what we might call
a "clear social fact." Relatives had complete faith in the
social organization of medical inquiry which produced proclamations of death, so that for the physician to announce
that a person was dead made it so. It is not clear that it is
the physician's authority which provides the fact of a death
with such a status, nor is there any basis for arguing that it
was the manner of his delivery of news of death that made
it so unquestionable. Unfortunately no evidence is available
which would permit us to answer the questions: What if the
hospital janitor were to announce the death?, What if the
physician were to announce it with hesitancy, "We think
your father died," or "It is our opinion that your father
died." The conditions for the "clarity" of this piece of news
cannot be offered, though it is to be noted that, in their announcement, physicians delivered the news with authority
and complete surety, and that other staff members are not
permitted to make such announcements. I would suspect that
were the physician to say "We think your father died," that
would be most upsetting to a relative. Persons expect, with
respect to death, that there is no question whatsoever, that

one is or one isn't, an expectation which seems to operate
for only a few matters, another of which, in the hospital,
appears to be the sex of a newborn. (Although here we observe the curious practice of holding up an infant in the hospital nursery and purposefully exposing its genitals, so that
parents can have a look for themselves.)

Let me now turn to the details of the announcement of
death occasion, taking up the analysis with the opening lines
of this encounter and exploring the unfolding structure of
the occasion. In announcing the death, the physician makes
his announcement forthrightly, with no circuity in the conduct of the delivery of the actual news. By the manner of
his seriousness when he enters the scene, he seems to effectively inhibit any byplay between relatives or overtures directed toward him. Relatives were observed to sit quietly as
he began to talk, no questions were initially asked, no exchanges of politenesses seen. The scene became defined, from
the first moment, as an occasion of utmost seriousness. Generally, the doctor's announcement of the death was made
within the first two sentences, usually in the course of one
long sentence.

In his presentation, more common in the DOA situation
than in announcements of deaths of hospital patients, he
tried to provide, in some way, that the death be seen as having followed a course of "dying." In nearly every scene I
witnessed, the doctor's opening remarks contained an historical reference. Some examples were:

> "Mrs. Jones, apparently Mr. Jones had a heart attack this after-
> noon and his body was too weak to fight it and he passed away."

> "It seems that in this accident your son's chest was broken and a
> rib probably punctured the heart area and he could not survive that
> kind of injury."

> "Your husband apparently had a stroke or heart attack and his
> system was not capable of surviving it. He passed away before he
> reached the hospital."

"It seems that there must have been a massive rupture of the heart, Mrs. Smith. Your husband died upon arrival at the hospital."

"From what we can tell it appears as though he must have been suffering from a heart ailment and apparently this time the attack was too strong for his system."

In none of the instances I observed was the relative told of the death in a sentence which included no reference to some medically relevant causal antecedent. This was true in accidental as well as "natural" deaths, and was true whether or not the physician had any basis for assuming a likely cause of death.

The greatest proportion of DOA cases are known to be heart attack victims, and in the event that there was no accident, nor any sign which would obviously rule out a heart attack, the physician generally says, "We're not sure but it might have been a heart attack," or some other remark containing reference to a likely cause. There were no instances of simply, "Your husband died," without some qualifying additions. In such situations, physicians seemed to feel that historicizing their delivery of news, no matter how limited their knowledge of the case, helped not only to reduce some of the shock value of "sudden deaths," but aided in the very grasp of the news. The correctness of the physician's supposed cause of death was of secondary significance relative to the sheer fact that he provided some sequential formulation of it, some means whereby the occurrence could be placed in a sequence of natural or accidental events. This was felt to be particularly necessary in the DOA circumstance, where many deaths occurred with no apparent "reason," particularly the "sudden, unexpected deaths." It seems that physicians felt that persons (and perhaps themselves as well), in order to have a beginning comprehension of what had occurred, needed some causally portrayed version.

After the death was announced, there characteristically

occurred a period in which the physician remained silent and
the relative engaged in some display of shock, dismay and
disorientation. Comparing the extent and form of emotional
responses to announcements of death in various circumstances, I found a considerable amount of variability. On
some occasions there was no crying whatever; the doctor's
mention of the death was responded to with downward-look-
ing silence. On other occasions, his utterance "passed away,"
or "died" spontaneously produced hysterical crying, screaming, moaning and trembling. I have observed relatives, particularly women, fall to the floor, loudly moaning and crying,
intermittently cursing, shaking and screaming. In numerous
instances I have seen men and women tear at themselves,
pulling their hair, tugging at their garments, biting their lips.

The form of the initial reaction to the death's announcement, both in its overall tonal character and duration, is
fairly well predictable. A combination of the following attributes would expectably produce a thoroughly explosive
response: a young, only child's sudden accidental death announced to his or her young Negro mother. At the other end
of a possible continuum of expressive behavior, the announcement of a long-term, chronically ill, white, Protestant woman's death to her upper-middle-class nephew, would be
likely characterized by a considerably less traumatic response.

Differences in emotional response are predictable by physicians and nurses and are explained by them through reference to a variety of common sense sociological and psychiatric bereavement theories. The doctor and nurse discussed
responses to death in terms of their theories of: 1) subcul-
tural, racial definitions of appropriate grief, 2) family social
structure, 3) the generalized social loss value of the deceased, 4) expectability of the death as an independent vari-
able, 5) psychoanalytical theories of guilt, etc.

Hospital staff spent a good deal of time in talking among

themselves about responses to death. There was considerable bull session interpretation of variations in emotional response to death, and hospital personnel often invoked their own experiences with death as elaborations or support of their theories. A good deal of this interpretation involved moral judgments as well, "These Negroes don't know how to control themselves," "Now, that's taking it like a man."

For important reasons, however, the expectations staff members held of the relative's likely response to the death did not directly structure the character of the announcement occasion and the doctor's activity in it. While experienced physicians came to expect differences in responses, and oriented their manner of informing the relative in light of the news' expectable reception (the task of having to inform a young mother of her child's death was considered more touchy and fraught with unpleasantness than the announcement of an older person's death), there were definite limits on the extent to which doctors could employ their expectations to structure the interaction in the setting.

A presumption of moral integrity is granted the immediately bereaved which, at least for a reasonable time period, is not considered to be invalidated should his behavior and appearance appear inconsistent with his status. The immediately bereaved person who does not cry or engage in other recognizable displays of grief, is nonetheless regarded as grievous. This is clearly indicated in our tendency to characterize such persons as those who "take it well," the implication clearly being that they are "taking it," but "showing it" less obviously. A key problem in interacting with newly bereaved persons, particularly at the very beginning of the death announcement occasion but generally confronted in a wide variety of situations, is the detection of that point at which it would be permissible to regard them as having the capacity and desire to show respect for normally constituted forms of interaction. This problem resides in the fact that any overture to interaction can be taken as premature, its prematurity lying in the possibility that the bereaved person is not yet to be held to respect some orderly form of interaction as governing his conduct.

With the announcement of a death and the creation of his status as a bereaved person, the relative enjoys the right to at least temporarily suspend his concern for normal requirements of demeanor, attentiveness, grace, deference, respect for the setting; in sum, with a properly situated composure. He has a right to expect that others will respect his position. This poses an interesting problem. There exists no easily employed rule for assessing the relation between the bereaved's appearances and his state of mind; appearances of calmness cannot be readily taken to represent the recipient's emotional composure. This ambiguity of appearances is seen in the everpresent threat that the appearance of composure constitutes merely an appearance, and any effort to take the appearance as corresponding to an underlying composure might be met with the response which says, "you have a lot of nerve to regard me as calm just because I don't show my grief." An example of such a response appeared in the San Francisco *Chronicle,* where a husband of a murdered woman, perhaps because of his own possible implication in her death, is reported to have said: "I'm outwardly calm because I'm taking sedatives. Inside I'm grieving more than anyone will ever know." It is of course important to note that the bereaved's right to grieve, while rather freely given, is not altogether immune to attack. Such rights must be somewhat earned, and persons who find it difficult or impossible to produce tears may be deeply troubled by what this says about their sense of loss.

Let me depart from the main concern, with the interaction structure of the announcement occasion, to comment briefly on some general aspects of this interpretative ambiguity. This problem is differently experienced in different points in the course of bereavement and is more or less troublesome depending upon the relationship between the immediately bereaved and other interactants. In the announcement of death scene itself, at a point so close to the receipt of the news, nonbereaved persons feel difficulty in engaging the immediately bereaved in any talk whatsoever. The bereaved is, at this point and at least for a short while thereafter, entitled to nearly complete disregard for proprieties governing interaction. That right, to be "out of it," is of short duration however, and persons unable to "pull themselves together" with reasonable rapidity, or at least refrain from public crying, will soon be the object of medical and psychiatric treatment, as well as less masked forms of sanctioning. During periods following the first days of the death, the problem of the bereaved's readiness to interact and the proper use of inferences in the interpretation of his appearances, takes on a different character. What seems to happen is that immediately bereaved persons are regarded as persons with whom it is improper to engage in sociable conversation, to treat in conversation matters of everyday life. The bereaved is regarded as one for whom appropriate talk is to be restricted to "death relevant matters." For what can be a long time after a death, persons tread carefully in interaction with the immediately bereaved, exhibiting caution in initiating talk about matters of general conversational value.

Particularly in American society, where bereaved persons do not wear visible insignia, it is problematic for them and others what the proper relevance of their own status for conversation ought to be. Bereaved persons have expressed the view that while they often seek to have their status lose its prominence in others' eyes, others feel obliged to take their cues from the bereaved before undertaking nonsympathetic conversation. Bereaved persons have reported that a great advantage in having close relatives nearby is that with

them, those who share their status as bereaved, they can
talk about other things. It is characteristic for bereaved persons to take the first step in relieving pressure on the non-
bereaved, which they frequently do by purposefully directing
the conversation to matters concerning the nonbereaved.
The sympathy phone calls I have managed to overhear all
seem to have the prevalent feature that there is a forced
distribution of interest. After the offer of sympathy has been
made, the bereaved directs a question to the sympathizer,
"How are your children these days?" or otherwise attempts
to take the center of attention from the fact of his own bereaved status by making small talk.

Bereaved persons apparently have considerable difficulty
in managing the rules of their own situation. They frequently
don't know at what point they should undertake activities
which were typically engaged in prior to the death. A large
part of their difficulty derives from the sheer fact of their
known status as a bereaved, which leaves them open for being treated sorrowfully, no matter how they might conduct
themselves. It is felt that only "with time" do they lose their
status as bereaved in the eyes of others and cease to be
treated as a grievous person. That time can often come long
after they have ceased regarding themselves in that fashion.
The proprieties governing the treatment of such persons,
continually places the burden upon them of demonstrating
their readiness for normal treatment.

A contrary strain operates at the same time, namely that
in anticipation of the sympathy gestures of others, the bereaved person feels obliged to appear sufficiently grievous
as to warrant offers of condolences. Bereaved persons must
be cognizant of the fact that for others their bereavement
may be more relevant than it is for themselves. These others
are not in a position to properly assume that the impact of
the death has lost its force. The anticipation of treatment
by others as a bereaved person very often operates to keep

the bereaved person in a bereaved status. This phenomenon is clearly seen in use of the telephone. Here the bereaved may have little control over getting involved with a would-be-sympathizer. Bereaved persons have reported that they find it necessary, often for an extended period of time after the death, to answer the phone with a sufficiently remorseful tone to appear properly deserving of the sympathy which a caller may be about to offer. They must be careful not to be caught off guard with a pleasant "hello" and be left with nothing to say or made to feel particularly awkward.

It can be argued that a key function of those social gatherings which occur shortly after the time of death is to expedite the process of receiving incoming gestures of sympathy. Without such gatherings, many more sympathizers must be encountered one by one, over an extended period of time after the death. The more a contact of this sort is removed from the time of the death, the more work must go into the mutual management of the death's relevance for conversation in it. Attendance at the funeral does not appear to relieve a sympathizer from his obligation to offer condolences, for that offer must generally be made in a more direct and personal fashion. A standard practice in American society which substitutes for the practice of wearing visible insignia of mourning, is for the immediately bereaved to go into isolation. Such an isolation must be sufficiently extensive so that upon the bereaved person's reemergence into public life, the relevance of the death has dissipated. Both he and others can then manage ordinary interaction with less strain.

To return to the announcement of death occasion, it is thus to be noted that the key problem which confronts each party, physician and relative, is the management of the "ambiguity of appearances." Both parties must be especially sensitive to the possibility that the bereaved may express his bereavement in a variety of ways.[6] While physicians and nurses may theorize about those who "take it well," "act like babies," "are too emotional," in the actual announcement occasion itself the doctor must give the bereaved person full license to express his grief as he sees fit. He must be careful not to move too quickly from that point at which he announces the death to a discussion of other matters. Should the relative not appear upset, the doctor must nonetheless treat him as though he is upset. To treat him otherwise is to risk the possibility of prematurely enforcing requirements for composure. While in ordinary social interaction we rely upon the way another appears as our evidence for how he feels and how we can properly treat him, in this setting such evidence is specifically difficult to act upon.

Because of this interpretative ambiguity, it is the bereaved person who must make the first move. It is he who must take the physician off the hook, spare him the discomfort of witnessing the bereaved's pain or the discomfort of waiting for expressions of pain to appear when they might not be strongly felt. In the course of the "bereavement career," the announcement of death is the first of a series of polite engagements, wherein the conditions of interaction require appropriate modulation of sentiments and appropriate regard for the other's situation of discomfort.

The bereaved person's right to be "out of it" is respected by the physician, who must tread carefully in initiating any interaction, lest that initiation appear premised on the recipient's "recovery," an assumption that the recipient might not want made about his behavior. While the informed relative is actively engaged in crying, weeping, sobbing or moaning, the doctor maintains as passive a stance as possible. He looks away and says nothing. Occasionally physicians employed the procedure of turning around, leaving their backs to the crying relative. The doctor doesn't smoke, nor does he look over any papers he might have in his hands. Neither does he exhibit any marked casualness in demeanor, like propping a foot up on a chair or table. He usually remains silently standing.

In none of the cases I have observed did the physician touch the relative or attempt to say anything while the relative was crying. No sympathetic remarks or gestures of sorrow were offered during the earliest period following his announcement. Sometimes the announcement was phrased sympathetically, "I'm sorry to have to tell you that your father passed away this morning"; at the end of the encounter, the physician often takes leave of the relatives with "I'm sorry." During telephone announcements of death, if the relative sobs, cries loudly or remains silent, the doctor remains silent himself.

While no sympathy gestures are made, neither does the doctor withdraw from the scene altogether by leaving the room, as other bearers of sad news may do. The doctor is concerned that the scene be contained and that he has some control over its progress, that it not follow him out into the hall. In nearly all cases the first genuine interchange of remarks was initiated by the relative. During the period of crying, if there is any, relatives frequently "talk." Examples were: "I can't believe it," "It's just not fair," "Goddamn," "Not John . . . no. . . ." These remarks were not responded to because they were not addressed to anyone. Frequently, they were punctuated by crying. The physician remains silent.

With relatives who do not express audible signs of despair, there is, at the outset, a system of mutual disattending as well. The relative looks away from the doctor and the doctor avoids confronting the relative's line of vision. In such instances there is usually a prolonged period of silence.

It is useful to consider the role of embarrassment in this setting. It is not permissible to withhold information about another's death because the knowledgeable person wishes to avoid embarrassing the uninformed by forcibly bringing him to tears. The physician has the problem of having to relate the occurrence of the death, minimizing the possibility that the relative will become embarrassed by his crying and, at the same time, he must insure that he retain control over the occasion. While he isolates the affair from the visibility of onlookers, he himself must occupy the position of an outsider. Yet he cannot remove himself from the setting and still accomplish other tasks, instructing relatives regarding funeral obligations, obtaining an autopsy permit (in hospital patient deaths), and generally controlling the encounter so that it doesn't generate into an explosive scene. While persons appear readily able to cry spontaneously in the presence of a stranger when delivered news of a death, and while embarrassment must not be made to inhibit the physician, it seems that the potentiality for embarrassment still strongly exists. Public crying can be sustained for only a rather short period of time before the cryer senses not only his own embarrassment but that which he is creating for others by not being able to effectively isolate himself from them and thereby release them from having to witness his grief.

The point at which genuine verbal interaction reoccurs is initiated at that moment where the relative can provide some demonstration of his own readiness to undertake conversation. Persons who did not cry were seen to engage in various maneuvers such as building into their behavior the possibility that a shift would occur in it. Such a shift constituted an appropriate indication of their readiness to move from crying to other matters. So, for example, some relatives made it a point to look away or turn around, or lower their heads after they were informed of the death, allowing them to later realign their eyes and bodies to meet the physician's awaiting presence. In this, the physician assisted them, himself looking away to make it easier for them to withdraw and then return. The recipient of the news felt that he could not rely on his momentary composure, that in itself not providing sufficient basis for the physician to regard him as "recovered" or "not upset." Some more positive demonstration of readiness, as with the use of a sequence, must be employed.

The initiation of "talk" usually properly begins realignment and the physician maintains himself ready to accept such a demonstration of readiness while, at the same time, allowing for initial failures in it. Should the recipient attempt to say something and burst into tears, the doctor acts as though the attempt was never made. Frequently, the recipient's first attempt utilized his own embarrassment and the uneasiness he perceived he was creating for the doctor, via an apology for "carrying on so." If the apology was accompanied by actual composure which the physician detected as potentially stable, he assured the recipient that "no apologies are necessary." This exchange then served to provide the first bridge toward a realignment of mutually oriented activity. Generally, the physician tended to be overcautious and preferred to wait as long as possible before accepting a gesture of readiness. In one case with which I am familiar, a man was told of his mother's death and exhibited absolutely no alteration in his appearance or composure. The man instead came right back with "I was expecting it to happen soon," put in quite flat, unemotional and forthright tones. He didn't flinch at all and there was no apparent sorrow in his remark. The physician appeared uneasy and simply looked down at the floor. Gradually, the man followed him by looking downward, covered his head with his arms, and remained silent for about a minute. Then he looked up, as simultaneously did the doctor, and made an opening remark. For a moment or two there was a considerable strain as the physician attempted to regard the man as somewhat unaware of what was told to him. Rather than repeat the announcement, he employed his own body to indicate his respect for the bereaved and the situation of bereavement, and the "bereaved" man followed in turn to act in appreciation.

"Talk" typically begins with an overture by the relative for some form of information. While there seems to be no particular preference for order, the following items were raised in a very great majority of cases:

1. *The matter of cause:* In the DOA circumstance particularly, the relative is likely to begin by asking, in one or another version, "Why did he die, doctor?" This occurred despite the fact that the doctor's announcement of the death contained a historical, causally couched reference to the death. In general, medical ward deaths, especially with patients whose condition had been a previous topic of conversation between the doctor and relative, the physician will often raise the issue of cause by restating a previous diagnosis, posed now as the most likely interpretation of the death. The following remark, recorded from a telephone announcement, is typical of this way of introducing the issue of cause:

> Apparently his heart became particularly strained during the night and, as we expected he might, he must have had another attack. As you know he was very weak and that's why his system couldn't tolerate this new attack.

In responding to the DOA relative's query about why he died, the announcing doctors often attempted to propose a tentative answer and then ask some questions themselves. The physician will often respond to a query with a remark on the order of "from the looks of it, he seemed to have had a general heart attack," and then ask a question like the following actual one:

"Did your father have a history of heart attacks?"

"Yes, for about twelve years."

Whereupon the subject of prior illness was dropped. Another doctor asked the relative of a DOA:

"Had your wife been under the care of a physician?"

To which the husband answered:

"For about seven months now. She was in the hospital for three weeks early in April."

The subject of her prior medical care was not pursued. In still another DOA instance, the intern asked the wife of a younger man who was brought in dead, moments before:

"Did he have medical trouble before?"

The wife, starting to cry again, answered:

"I don't know what it could have been."

Her remark terminated the discussion of prior medical history.

It is instructive to contrast these forms of lay-medical interaction about illness and medical history with that more commonly encountered format of interaction of the physical examination or medical history taking on a patient. In the latter setting, the physician is concerned to follow through a given line of inquiry, record reported facts, and seek a consistent and detailed account of the background on the case. So that a remark like "she was in the hospital for three weeks in April" could be expected to be followed, in the usual hospital circumstance, by a next question such as "what was she treated for then?" and that followed by an additional one until he obtained a sufficient account about the matter in question to premise his own diagnostic and treatment activities. The account "I don't know what it could be," in an encounter between physician and relative about a recent emergency admission of a live patient, would be expectably pursued with a remark on the order of "why don't you first tell me what you know and then we can try to see what it is?"

When gathering material in a medical history the physician is concerned, as he is not here, with checking information for its consistency, filling out lines of reported data with more detail, assessing the reliability of the reporter's ac-

count, ignoring irrelevant descriptions, pursuing lines of
lineage in the hereditary medical history, gathering information about the specific character of the patient's former
medical treatment and generally, covering that whole range
of matters which physicians cover when they are doing medical interviewing, diagnosis and research.

In his "discussion" of causes or possible antecedents with
the relatives of the recently pronounced DOA, or his mention of likely causes with the relative of a recently deceased
hospital patient on the medical or surgical wards, his "inquiry" takes a radically nonmedical character. While the
sentences he utters may be lexically the same as those he
might utter when conducting a medical history interview,
they are nonetheles asked differently. They are not followed
through; they appear disjunctive; any given question does
not appear to follow the previous one, so that he need not
rely on an "answer" to know how to direct the next remark.
They are not recorded; he shows no special interest in any
specific question or its answer; he shows no concern to move
to another area; he allows any question to be answered
rather than interrupt should the answer appear not to address the question. Any answer is accepted as just as "relevant" as any other. The line of his "inquiry" is thus markedly set off from "medical inquiry" as a method of eliciting
"information." As a first statement, it may be said that in
the death circumstance the physician is *making talk*.

Not only are the physician's questions not asked medically, despite the lexically medical reference, they are not
heard as medical questions. The same lexical utterance, "did
he have medical trouble before?" made in the conduct of a
medical history interview of a patient's relative, when heard
as a medical question will be answered with the concern to
address the implied medical relevance of it. People listen to
physicians' remarks about their prior condition or that of
their relatives as grounds for offering elaboration, providing

detail to the doctor, thinking over what they recall in their or their relatives' histories of treatments and symptoms, reporting confusion they have about those histories. The very possibility of a medical interview rests upon the mutual sense both parties to it have of the medically relevant aspects of a question. For physicians to ask the kinds of questions they do, like "Why don't you tell me what's wrong with you," respondents must know what it means to answer a medical question, must learn what it is to report symptoms, in sum, must learn how to talk to doctors and hear doctors' remarks. While the domain of interests, concerns, worries and technical knowledge differs for both layman and physician, the possibility of doctor-patient-relative communication rests upon a proper mutual orientation to the sense of each other's remarks.

In examining the interchange between doctor and relative after the death's occurrence was announced and when talk became directed to that fact, I found that the questions that were asked and the remarks offered as answers, regardless of who it was that did the answering or asking, have the quality of "making talk" about the event of the death. Utterances lexically similar to those routinely encountered in medical-lay communication, are here structured within the framework of a conversational style. It can be said of the interchange as a whole, that it resembles "mere talk". To provide further illustrations of this character to the interaction, let me give additional examples from the other domains of "topics" regularly found in the announcement of death occasion.

2. *The matter of pain:* The concern over whether or not the deceased experienced any pain before his death is typically voiced by the relative, who asks (and here the specific words employed are extremely similar from one such setting to another) : "Did he have much pain before he died, doctor?" In reviewing my field notes on the announcements I

find that in only a handful of these occasions did the immediately bereaved fail to form a question regarding the deceased's pain before death. Universally, it seems, the doctor
answers "No," when asked if pain was experienced and in
most instances provides a form of "elaboration" which the
following recorded comment typified:

> "He was under heavy sedation right until the end and I can assure
> you that he experienced no discomfort at all."

With such a comment, the issue of pain is apparently settled.
Never did there occur any further interrogation by the relative, nor any greater degree of elaboration by the physician.
The striking fact about the "discussion" of pain is its
marked uniformity from one particular scene to another.
This uniformity is most interesting in light of the fact that
the actual circumstances of the deaths differed widely with
respect to the extent and manner of pain experienced by the
"dying" patient. While doctors therefore routinely and purposefully lie in their characterizations of many deaths as
painless, more importantly, relatives who in fact knew that
the death was painful nonetheless asked the question about
pain and let go unchallenged the physician's comment on its
painlessness. In DOA circumstances the physician's elaboration on the question of pain usually takes this form:

> "He probably had a massive heart attack and with these things
> there is hardly any pain because it is so quick."

In one case, a man had a heart attack at home which was
witnessed by the family. The ambulance driver reported to
me that when he arrived at the home the man was lying on
the floor gripping his chest and moaning. The man died in
the ambulance on the way to the hospital and was pronounced dead upon arrival. The relatives asked the doctor
whether or not much pain was experienced, to which he answered "no" and gave the account quoted above. The rela-

tives then proceeded to inquire about what they were to "do now" and the topic of conversation turned to the procedures of contacting a mortician and having him call the coroner's office.

In another case the matter of pain was "discussed" between the pronouncing physician and the wife of a long-term, chronically ill, cancer patient. The woman had spent much of the year prior to the death of her husband at his bedside, long periods of which involved the not uncommon task of having to witness the moaning in pain that often characterizes the lot of these patients. Yet her reference to his pain and the physician's assurance of its absence, came off in its typically standardized way, with very little variation from any other announcement of death occasion. She didn't say, as she "might" have, "What do you mean *no pain,* after all I've gone through . . ."; nor did the physician remark, as he "might" have, "You know he felt pain, you certainly saw him suffer with it, cancer is always painful."

3. *Matters of preventability:* In a great number of the announcements, the issue of the possible forestallment of the death or its preventability, became "topical" via the physician's comment:

> "Of course we did everything we could. There was nothing that could have been done at this point."

Such a statement was nearly without exception answered by some version of "Yes, of course, Doctor, I understand. We appreciate everything you've done." In none of the cases with which I am familiar was the assertion of the inevitability of death "under the circumstances" not provided by the physician nor "accepted" by the relative. At least in my experience, doctors did not qualify their claims that "everything was done," nor did relatives question their not doing so. Of course, while it happens that legal suits of negligence are sometimes instituted, I am not prepared to consider the

manner in which they arise. In the settings with which I am
acquainted there occurred no instances where one could detect in the character of the doctor-relative interchange the
basis of distrust, suspicion or anger which might be regarded
as preliminary to such action. Whatever such efforts might
have been taken, and my data does not follow through cases
sufficiently to locate such efforts, did not seem to be framed
within the context of the announcement occasion. To the
contrary, the interchange of remarks concerning the death's
preventability were uniform with respect to their standardized, almost staged character.

With the above outline of "things discussed" in mind, let
me consider, in general terms, the matter of "talking about
death," and the "conversational" character of the doctor-
relative encounter. If one searches the medical world for
that setting where doctors appear to act least like doctors
and relatives least like "relatives of patients," the announcement of death occasion seems to offer itself as a paradigmatic locale. The striking character of the doctor-relative
"talk" here is that it sounds nonmedical. Concerns for demonstrations to be adequate, for consistency of fact, for completeness, relatedness, relevance—those interests which govern medical interviews, work-ups, diagnostic conferences
—were absent.

In the doctor-relative encounter, the talk which occurs is
such that rules of conversation come to govern its production, and the matter being talked about stands as the merely
occasioned topic of conversation.[7] By "occasioned topic" I
mean the topic which the occasion provides as the appropriate matter to discuss. Physician and relative, under the
circumstances of a death, cannot discuss family intimacies
(at least not in the DOA circumstances involving a ward
physician), the weather, the physician's work problems, the
state of the hospital's physical equipment. Their situation
prescribes that the death in question be the exclusive focus

of attention. The conversation has a severely restricted content. In constructing talk in a clearly conversational idiom, without respect for concerns for consistency, completeness and medical relevance, the parties attempt to handle their differing perspectives on the event. Rather than talk about the event of the death directly, they institute a little piece of sociable conversation. While the content is restricted to be sure, the essential property of the talk, its conversationally structured sequencing, stands out over and above the fact of the death.

In the announcement of death, there gradually occurs a transformation from that state of crying, moaning or distracted silence with which the encounter opens, to a sequence of conversational exchange, wherein rules of polite discourse are instated. The prominent feature of the "talk" is seen in the fact that while in engaging in it, acting in accord with the rules which govern polite interchange, following a give and take sequence, leaving the engagement with respect shown for conventional modes of leave taking, distributing the talk among the participants, persons find themselves involved in a recognizable form of regular social conduct. The sheer fact of conducting a conversation in situations where talk might appear as a strange activity, namely when a close relative has just been announced as dead, locates the event, despite its tragic character, as a nonetheless handleable matter. In talking, persons affirm their sense of the essential stability of their conditions. To "talk," where "talk" means abiding by conventions of speech, responsiveness of demeanor, the alignment of eyes and bodies, the exchange of politenesses, waiting for the other to stop before beginning oneself, is to demonstrate that grasp over one's self as prevails in the ordinary conduct of daily affairs.

The function of "talk" in situations of trauma was perhaps nowhere as elegantly depicted as by Tolstoy in his descriptions of the *Ancien Regime*. In 1805 and during the

Italian campaigns of the Bonaparte Revolution, Napoleon
is planning his invasion of Russia. In the opening scene of
War and Peace, Anna Pavlovna is having one of her famous
soirees, and Tolstoy has her greet a guest with the following remarks:

> Well prince, Genoa and Lucca are now no more than private
> estates of the Bonaparte family. No, I warn you, that if you do not
> tell me we are at war, if you again allow yourself to palliate all
> the infamies and atrocities of this Antichrist—upon my word I be-
> lieve he is—I don't know you in future, you are no longer my
> friend, no longer my faithful slave, as you say. There, how do you
> do, how do you do, I see I'm scaring you, sit down and talk to me.[8]

Tolstoy's insight, seen in the line "sit down and talk to me,"
was that in engaging in "talk," matters which otherwise
might produce severe immobility, upsettedness, consterna-
tion and fear could be overlaid by ordinary conventions of
interaction, and thereby have their sense incorporated within
and constrained by the requirements of conversational social
discourse. Throughout the first chapter of the book Tolstoy
has Anna Pavlovna engaged in the production of "talk."
War and Peace can be said to have as one of its central
themes the notion that in doing "talk," persons, as members
of a society, provide for the stability of the social world.
Perhaps Tolstoy's most elegant statement was:

> As the enemy drew nearer to Moscow the attitude taken by its
> inhabitants in regard to their position did not become more serious
> but, on the contrary, more frivolous, as is always the case with
> people who see a great danger approaching. At the approach of
> danger there are always two voices that speak with equal force in
> the heart of man: one very reasonably tells the man to consider
> the nature of the danger and the means of avoiding it; the other
> even more reasonably says that it is too painful and harassing to
> think of the danger, since it is not in a man's power to provide for
> everything and escape from the general march of events; and that it
> is therefore better to turn aside from the painful subject till it has

Send information on Program: No. 1 - 221.00 ( )   NEW REDUCED
                              No. 2 - 341.00 ( )   PRICES

                              No. 3 - 615.00 ( )   No. 1 - 200.00 ( )

                                                     No. 2 - 330.00 ( )

                                                     No. 3 - 597.00 ( )

Send information on College Credit ( )

I am interested in 1973 departure:

May 24:   N.Y.C. ( )   Chicago ( )   L.A. ( )   Oakland ( )   Portland ( )   Seattle ( )
May 31:   N.Y.C. ( )   Chicago ( )   L.A. ( )   Oakland ( )   Portland ( )   Seattle ( )
June 7:   N.Y.C. ( )   Chicago ( )   L.A. ( )   Oakland ( )   Portland ( )   Seattle ( )
June 14:   N.Y.C. ( )   Chicago ( )   L.A. ( )   Oakland ( )   Portland ( )   Seattle ( )
June 21:   N.Y.C. ( )   Chicago ( )   L.A. ( )   Oakland ( )   Portland ( )   Seattle ( )
June 28:   N.Y.C. ( )   Chicago ( )   L.A. ( )   Oakland ( )   Portland ( )   Seattle ( )

Please print or type:

Name _SANTOS CRIOS_   Phone _225-7074_   Age _39_

Address _5159 GROVEHILL_   _SAN ANTONIO,_   _TEXAS_   _78218_
            Street   City   State   Zip Code

come, and to think of what is pleasant. In solitude a man generally yields to the first voice; in society to the second. So it was now
with the inhabitants of Moscow. It was long since there had been
so much gaiety in Moscow as that year.[9]

The institutionalization of "sociable" talk or "conversation," here serves to provide a standardized way for bringing the participants into alignment and moving the encounter
about from its position of initial disturbance to that point
where a consideration of signing an autopsy permit, arranging for the disposition of the body, obtaining personal belongings may properly occur. In allowing himself to engage
in a conversation, the recipient demonstrates, at least temporarily, his willingness to sustain orderly enforceable forms
of interchange, in a relatively bureaucratic setting, with one
with whom no other current basis for interaction exists (the
continued mutual crying which two parents might be able to
do upon the death of their child when in the privacy of their
home, or, at the other end, the technically oriented discussion of medical fact which would otherwise be appropriate,
in the case of a live patient, between physician and relative).

Two parties, the County Hospital physician and the relative of a recently deceased person, manage, through this
brief interlude of sociable-like talk, to make their differing
perspectives on the meaning of the death temporarily irrelevant. The doctor, who in the back rooms has experimented
on the body, treating it as "just another DOA," manages
to convey to the relatives his respect for a deceased "loved
one," while at the same time discharging his obligations to
report the death. The relative, for whom the death has
an altogether different and deeper significance, manages,
through the brief interlude of politeness, to spare the physician from undue discomfort by checking his own emotions.
Should the relative feel less than horrified by the death, he
cooperates with the physician in constructing an appropriately solemn occasion. In such an instance, the two sustain

the fiction that an event of immense sorrow has transpired. In either case, whatever the actual distribution of feelings, full exposure of true sentiments and perspectives about the death is avoided in each party's concern to protect the other's integrity and insure his own.

VIII

An Overview

My central concern has been to describe the work conditions of the hospital environment and the place of "dying" and "death" within that occupational setting. By taking the perspective of an insider, I have tried to document facts of hospital life and death which have hitherto not been described. As a sociologist, I have been particularly interested in the study of social organization, and especially, in the ways in which the categories of "dying" and "death" are actually used within the work requirements imposed by staff members in their daily life on the ward.

It was in the course of daily hospital routines—handling bodies, administering the flow of incoming and outgoing patients, doing diagnosis, prognosis, medical experimentation and teaching—that certain patients became recognized as those who could properly be accorded special treatments, the "dying" and "death" treatments. Whatever a "dying" or "dead" patient might mean in other contexts, when patients were so designated at County, staff members felt they had license to act in accord, first and foremost, with considerations of efficiency. The mass methods of patient care in that institution, common in many of our publicly supported hospitals, was felt to require that processing be the major practical consideration.

While hospital personnel sustained detachment from "dying" and "death," it occurred, on some occasions, that routine procedures and attitudes became altered and upset. The successful daily management of "dying" and "dead" bodies seemed to require a relatively constant character to the social types of persons who comprised the patient population. So long as the patient whose death was anticipated or occurred was an elderly, poor and morally proper person, the occasion of his "dying" and "death" was treated with little special notice. On critical occasions, however, as when a child died, or when a successful, middle-class person was brought into the Emergency Unit as a DOA, ordinary procedures of treatment were not instituted. Members of the staff, on such occasions, lost something of their grasp on matters which they would have otherwise treated in the most perfunctory ways.

Nowhere was this disruption clearer than with the deaths of children. Nurses were observed to break down in tears when a child died, and in such cases "dying" and "death" temporarily lost their routinized meanings, activities and consequences. When an intoxicated, suicidal or "criminal" patient was treated, these persons' moral characters were prevalent considerations for staff members. Rather than "just another patient," the attitudes toward such persons ranged from vehemence, digust and horror to empathetic dismay. It can be noted, as a general sociological observation, that no matter how routinized an institution's methods for handling its daily tasks, those routines remain vulnerable at certain key points. At County, no matter how nonchalantly staff members managed to wrap a patient's body for discharge to the morgue, taper off in the administration of drugs and care to the "dying," or pronounce deaths and

return to other tasks, "special cases"—the morally "imper-
fect" and the especially "tragic"—upset those routines,
made them more difficult to carry off, more interestedly attended or substantially revised.

Perhaps in regarding these special cases, insight may be
gained into the requirements for usual, orderly ward activity. On those occasions when a special case caused staff members to step outside their attitudes of indifference and concerns for efficient organization, one could glimpse something
of an underlying capability for emotional involvement, a
capability which was regularly held in check. When on one
known occasion the nurse in the Emergency Unit with a
reputation as a "tough cookie" broke down in tears at the
death of a particularly handsome four-year-old child, some
evidence was given that her usual "toughness" was largely
a product of the requirements of the job, and not entirely
basic to her personality. Despite the great "efficiency" with
which the daily course of processing the "dying" and "dead"
proceeded, at critical points I found that I could make sense
of what was going on in the care of a patient only by con-
sulting that vaguely constituted motivational source referred
to by sociologists as the "cultural value." In selecting certain
deaths to invest with special meaning, staff members demonstrated that despite their work involvements in matters of
life and death, "death" nonetheless held a noninstitutionally
prescribed texture of meanings, an event which could call
forth grief and sympathy.

There occurred critical junctures at which discrepant attitudes with respect to "death," borne of widely differing
interests, came into contact and had to be managed. The key
juncture at County involved interactions between members
of the house staff and patients' families. I attempted to
sketch the dynamics which were observed in one such encounter, the announcement of death occasion. Here the physician, one for whom the DOA death was just another work

event, and an annoying one at that, found it necessary to convey an impression of soberness in face of a deeply troubled member of the public. While the body was in the back rooms being experimented upon and otherwise "processed," in the front office it had to be regarded as a "deceased loved one." That the physicians at County seemed to experience no special difficulty in moving back and forth between these attitudes does not necessarily attest to their "insincerity." Rather, it is the hospital situation as a frame of reference, and not the physician's emotional and personality makeup, which governs his manner in handling facts of life and death.

The method by which news of a death was disseminated, with paramount concern for speed, noncircuity and little in the way of an attempt to soften its impact, points to the general fact that with respect to some critical facts in the social world, commitment to a "reality orientation" becomes the only proper course of action. Throughout the course of interactions between physicians and relatives at County, the import of ascertained facts or likely facts was filtered through a series of tactful reconstructions. Accountability to members of the public was circumvented or restricted within tightly prescribed limits, either out of concern for the internal security of the medical world or so as to give "room for hope," no matter how hopeless the known circumstances may have been. With the occurrence of a death, from the physician's and hospital's standpoint at least, tactfulness, avoidance, circuity and other devices for avoiding direct confrontation were improper; the facts had to be laid bare, no matter what their expected reception or possible feedbacks. The resources of the institution for doing deceptive work, whether for its own protection or the public's had to be suspended. Institutions, as well as the individuals to whom they are accountable, must be prepared, at some critical points, for telling and hearing the undisguised worst. There are similar "unavoidable facts" in other areas: the businessman's disclosure of bankruptcy, the nation's declaration of war, the jury's pronouncement of sentence. Wherever such a "fact" is likely to occur, one may observe relevant parties to engage, where possible, in some preparatory work designed to pave the way for that point at which forthright disclosure will be required.

No matter how successful, however, the physician's efforts to have relatives regard the patient as "dying," death itself will always be, in an important sense, "sudden." At one moment the patient is alive and the next dead. So long as "death" is viewed as having such either-or properties, there will always be a critical point at which a radical alteration of previous states will be perceived, a point at which attempts to construct what has occurred along a temporal continuum will be strained. It is at that point when, from the physician's standpoint, the "facts are in" and unconcealed presentation is required. It appears that only in the religious domain can "death" be construed as a fact of unclear import, with more vaguely defined properties.

I would caution the reader in interpreting the scope of the findings reported in this study. I would argue that County Hospital is fairly representative of many publicly supported, general hospitals, and that the treatment of the "dying" and "dead" observed there is not, by any means, unique to that particular institution. Many observers have noted the perfunctory and often harsh manner in which the care of poor patients proceeds. I hope to have added to that documentation and perhaps to the general public's awareness of the specific ways in which the indigent are often treated. At the same time, I cannot offer myself as having sufficient knowledge of such institutions as a whole to adequately characterize patient care practices in them. While I feel reasonably certain that other investigators will find similar practices in many United States hospitals, and that many practicing nurses and physicians will recognize aspects

of "death" and "dying" care that I describe about County,
I must nonetheless caution against premature condemnation.

A more difficult task than that involved in specifying the
generality of the practices I have described, is that of assessing what might be done about them should they be widespread. There are many conflicting interests at stake. Those
who argue the need for liberalizing the physician's stance
toward euthanasia, certainly can make a good argument for
their case. At the same time, great caution must be exercised,
I would maintain, lest a rationale for euthanasia be permitted to make even more perfunctory the care for the "dying" than may now exist. I feel it would be premature to
propose any definite programs in this area. Rather, I would
argue that much more extensive research and consciousness
about patient care must precede policy making. In particular
I would argue the need for a closer and more nationwide
examination of how the deaths of patients are decided and
how the decisions that a patient is "dying" are made. I think
a careful look must be taken at the possibility of discrimina-
tory treatment in the care for the "dying" and "dead" based
upon social class and related variables. My experience at
Cohen Hospital clearly indicated to me that a considerable
difference in staff attitudes toward the "dying" and "dead"
exists between the county and private medical care institution. This is a possibility about which current public and
governmental concern must become increasingly sensitive. If
hospital costs can be legitimately subject to public review,
so can their practices of patient care. I hope to have made
a contribution toward beginning such a review, at least concerning "dying" and "death."

Notes

I. *Death in the Hospital*

[1] There is an extensive literature available on death. The best general source for literary treatments of death is F. Hoffman, "Mortality and Modern Literature," in H. Feifel, ed., *The Meaning of Death* (New York: McGraw Hill Book Company, 1959), pp. 133-157. For a recent contextual analysis of morbidity themes in literature, see L. Fiedler, *Love and Death in the American Novel* (New York: Meridian Books, 1960). As is often the case, literary descriptions far exceed in detail and sophistication, those of professional academics. Nowhere in the academic literature are death scenes described as vividly as in Hemingway's *A Natural History of the Dead,* or Mailer's *The Naked and the Dead.* And there is Orwell's "How the Poor Die," Rilke's *The Notebooks of Malte Laurids Brigge,* Tennyson's poem "The Children's Hospital," Tolstoy's *War and Peace,* and his "The Death of Ivan Ilyich," James Agee's *Death in the Family,* and Cather's *Death Comes for the Archbishop,* to mention but a few.

The anthropological literature on death and rituals surrounding its occurrence is too extensive to readily cite. The works of Durkheim, Frazer, Tylor, Evans-Pritchard, Malinowski, Radcliffe-Brown, Van Gennep, Hertz and Gluckman are obviously central. A relatively complete collection of death practices in non-Western societies may be found in E. Bendmann, *Death Customs* (New York: Alfred A. Knopf, Inc., 1930). The most serious study of death ritual by an anthropologist within the past twenty-five years is Jack Goody's *Death, Property and the Ancestors* (Stanford: Stanford University Press, 1962).

For recent popular discussions of funeral practices see particularly Leroy Bowman, *The American Funeral* (New York: Paperback Library, Inc., 1964), J. Mitford, *The American Way of Death* (New York: Simon and Schuster, Inc., 1963), and R. Harner, *The High Cost of Dying* (New York: Crowell-Collier Publishing Co., 1963). There have been sociological studies of occupational features of undertaker work, notable among which is R. Habenstein, *The American Funeral Director: A Study in the Sociology of Work,* unpublished doctoral dissertation, University of Chicago, 1954. A recent exception to the general absence of empirical research on death by sociologists is the work of Glaser and Strauss. See especially R. Glaser and A. Strauss, "Temporal Aspects of Dying as a Nonscheduled Status Passage," *American Journal of Sociology,* 81 (July, 1965), 48-59, and their recent book, *Awareness of Dying* (Chicago: Aldine Publishing Co., 1965).

There is a considerable literature on death and the family, but very little of it is based on concrete empirical investigations of family interaction in times of death, and most discussion is largely couched in psychiatric terms. Especially see T. Eliot, "The Bereaved Family," *Annals of the American Academy of Political and Social Science,* 160 (March, 1932), 184-190, K. Davis, "The Widow and the Social Structure," *American Sociological Review,* 5 (August, 1940), 635-647, H. Becker, "The Sorrow of Bereavement," *Journal of Abnormal and Social Psychology,* 27 (1933), 391-410, and G. Gorer, *Death, Grief and Mourning* (Garden City: Doubleday & Company, Inc., 1965).

The psychiatric literature, as that of the anthropologists, is quite extensive. The most prominent sources are S. Freud, "Thoughts for the Times on War and Death," *Collected Papers* (London: Hogarth Press, 1948), 4, *Civilization and its Discontents* (London: Hogarth Press, 1933), *Totem and Taboo* (New York: W. W. Norton & Company, Inc., 1952), *Mourning and Melancholia* (London: Hogarth Press, 1957) ; S. Anthony, *The Child's Discovery of Death* (London: Routledge & Kegan Paul, Ltd., 1940) ; W. Bromberg and P. Schilder,

"The Attitude of Psychoneurotics towards Death," *Psychoanalytic Review*, 23, No. 1 (International Universities Press, 1955); M. Klein, "Mourning and its Relation to Manic-Depressive States," *International Journal of Psychoanalysis*, 21, (1940), 125-153; E. Lindemann, "Symptomatology and Management of Acute Grief," *American Journal of Psychiatry*, (Sept. 1941), 101-141.

The recently published collection of articles on hospital social structure, edited by E. Friedson, *The Hospital in Modern Society* (1963), contains no discussions of death, nor is there significant treatment of the topic in any other research on this institution, with the slight exception of the attention given "dying" by R. Fox, *Experiment Perilous* (1959). The most vivid account of the general hospital available, with exceedingly close attention given to details of daily hospital life, is Jan de Hartog's semi-fictional *The Hospital* (New York: Atheneum Publishers, 1964).

Research on medical students contains only minimal reference to the relevance of "dying" and "death" in environments of learning. See H. Becker, *et al., Boys in White* (Chicago: University of Chicago Press, 1961), and R. K. Merton, G. Reader, and P. Kendall eds., *The Student Physician* (Cambridge: Harvard University Press, 1957). Talcott Persons' famous articles on illness and the medical profession contain only indirect references to death and dying; his recent paper, "Death in American Society" has, as its central thesis, the notion that death is avoided, both by members of the society and investigators, for it constitutes a central threat to the stability of the social system in a society based on the Protestant ethic of achievement.

Recent collections of articles on death are almost exclusively given to semi-philosophical discussions and attitudinal research. See especially, H. Feifel, *op. cit.,* and R. Fulton, ed., *Death and Identity* (New York: John Wiley & Sons, Inc., 1965). For serious collections of major philosophical positions on death, see J. Choron, *Death and Western Thought* (New York: Collier Books, 1963), and A. Flew, *Body, Mind and Death* (New York: The Macmillan Company, 1964).

Only in the medical literature, those occasional articles written by practicing physicians about the social organization of their own circumstances or practice and the practically motivated researches of nursing personnel, does death regularly appear as a matter of interest.

Especially relevant are R. Bulger, "The Dying Patient and his Doctor," *Harvard Medical Alumni Bulletin,* **34**, No. 23 (1960) ; V. E. Frenkl, *The Doctor and Soul* (New York: Alfred A. Knopf, Inc., 1955) ; O. Guttentag, "The Meaning of Death in Medical Theory," *Stanford Medical Bulletin,* **17**, No. 4 (1959) ; A. H. Solnit, "Psychologic Considerations in the Management of Deaths on Pediatric Hospital Services," *Pediatrics,* **24**, No. 1, 106-115; C. K. Aldrich, "The Dying Patient's Grief," *Journal of the American Medical Association,* **184**, No. 5 (1963).

II. *The Setting of the County Hospital*

[1] It is a well documented fact that "charity" hospitals are not, in fact, free. For national figures on the percentage of hospital costs met by patients in such institutions, see J. H. Hayes, and H. Becker, *Financing Hospital Care in the United States,* 3 Vols. (New York: Blakiston, 1954), 52, and S. E. Harris, *The Economics of American Medicine* (New York: The Macmillan Company, 1964), 229-337.

[2] For an excellent description of a hospital with very many physical features apparently similar to County, see Jan De Hartog's account of a Houston, Texas, general hospital in *The Hospital* (New York: Atheneum Publishers, 1964).

[3] For general discussions of recruitment to internships and data on the location of medical students after graduation, see W. Glaser, "Internship Appointments of Medical Students," *Administrative Science Quarterly,* **4**, (December, 1959), 337-356, and J. E. Deitrick, *Medical Schools in the United States at Mid-Century* (New York: Macmillan Company, 1953), Chapter 14.

[4] Elsewhere I have reported my research on another organization wherein interchangeability of personnel and mass treatments were, as in County, prominent work features. See D. Sudnow, "Normal Crimes: Sociological Features of the Penal Code in a Public Defender Office," *Social Problems,* **12**, No. 3 (Winter, 1965), 255-276.

III. *Who Died?*

[1] For a discussion of these routine inventories in another hospital setting, see J. Emerson, "Social Functions of Humor in a Hospital,"

unpublished doctoral dissertation, University of California, Berkeley, 1964, especially Chapter V, "Laughing at Death."

[2] It is a matter of general sociological interest that a significant transformation occurs when an event comes to be seen as having ordinal properties, i.e., where it is not merely an occurrence but one which is seen as an event in a series. A major shift in the institution of marriage, for example, can be said to attend talk of a "first marriage." In the hospital, experience with such events as giving injections or administering enemas, while perhaps producing skill in doing so, is not conversationally additive as a competence-attesting matter, so that having given one is just as good as having given a hundred. The analysis of those ways in which persons numerically characterize events in their environments has been neglected by sociologists, who generally employ numerical characterizations, under the auspices of their statistical procedures, without seeking to fit the properties of such numerical systems to the properties of the objects they describe from the standpoint of the subject.

[3] It is to be pointed out that the use of this way of talking can be presumptuous for one who, in fact, has not been around very long. "Having lost count," while in any given case perhaps accurately descriptive, is not thereby useable. It is not so much the usage's correctness which warrants it, but what that usage says about its user's claims to certain membership statuses; entitlement to it may be based on other facts: like, for example, the user's status in the group in which it is used. Among others of his own station an intern will talk of "having lost count" but should an elderly physician be present, an inappropriate disregard for his place as a novitiate in the world of medicine might be conveyed.

[4] Numerous examples of patient awareness of death are given in the literature. One study gives the following:

> Three hours elapsed before another nurse came in to discover the death. In the meantime the three living patients had to exist with the horror of one of their number lying dead and uncovered among them.

In R. H. Blum, *et al., The Management of the Doctor-Patient Relationship* (New York: McGraw-Hill Book Company, 1960), p. 215.

And Orwell, in his "How the Poor Die," writes:

I could see old Numero 57 lying crumpled up on his side, his face stick-
ing out over the side of the bed, and towards me. He had died some
time during the night, nobody knew when. When the nurses came they
received news of his death indifferently and went about their work.
After a long time, an hour or more, two other nurses marched in
abreast like soldiers, with a great clumping of sabots, and knotted up
the corpse in the sheets, but it was not removed till some time later.

G. Orwell, "How the Poor Die," in *Shooting an Elephant* (New
York: Harcourt, Brace & World, Inc., 1950), p. 215.

[5] In such institutions as sanitariums, with largely ambulatory patients, the removal of bodies must be more secretly conducted. Mann
provides a fictional account:

. . . they are very discreetly managed, you understand; you hear nothing of them, or only by chance afterwards; everything is kept strictly
private when there is a death, out of regard for other patients, especially the ladies, who might easily get a shock. You don't notice it,
even when somebody dies next door. The coffin is brought in very early
in the morning, while you are asleep, and the person in question is
fetched away at a suitable time too—for instance, while we are eating.

T. Mann, *The Magic Mountain* (New York: Alfred A. Knopf,
Inc., 1958), p. 53.

[6] The stated reason for this universal feature of hospital architecture
is that the morgue must be readily accessible to the street to aid in
convenient transport of bodies to funeral hearses, and so situated that
others will not happen upon it:

The hospital morgue is best located on the ground floor and placed in
an area inaccessible to the general public. It is important that the unit
have a suitable exit leading onto a private loading platform which is
concealed from hospital patients and the public.

J. K. Owen, *Modern Concepts of Hospital Administration* (Philadelphia: W. B. Saunders Co., 1962), p. 304. Nearly without exception nurses purposefully avoided going near the morgue, and several
persons who worked in that wing of the hospital whose parking facilities were adjacent to the morgue, purposefully parked their cars at
more inconvenient places to avoid having to pass the morgue landing
on their way into the building.

[7] Students of occupations have given attention to the visibility of
activities in the appearance of some known person on some scene. The
morgue attendant's identity and the known occurrence of an event by

way of his appearance are based upon personal acquaintance, or "knowing who he is," coupled with the semi-public definition of his activities as tightly circumscribed to picking up bodies and doing autopsies. He thus differs, sociologically, from those from whom others obtain information by virtue of a uniform, or by way of particular historical knowledge of some concrete scene in which the appearance of a particular other has special significance. The fact of his only being semi-publicly known as the morgue attendant, i.e., only to members of the staff, constituted one of "John's" only freedoms, that he could pass before members of the outside public without being noticeably different from other attendants. For a relevant discussion of general strategies of "passing" and the problems of persons having stigmas of various sorts, see E. Goffman, *Stigma* (Englewood Cliffs, N.J.: Prentice-Hall, Inc., 1963), especially Chapter 3.

[8] There are some significant exceptions, however, all of which have to do with the fact that in surgery the protection of the patient from germs is considered important, while in the autopsy it is only the operators' health that is important. So, for example, there is no sterilization of instruments. The masks that are worn are for the operators' protection, not for the "patient's."

[9] Hospital morgues are reported to serve other functions, as well, among them being as field training centers for student undertakers, as in the case of New York's Bellevue Hospital. See S. Cutolo, *Bellevue Is My Home* (Garden City: Doubleday & Company, Inc., 1956), p. 161.

IV. *Social Death*

[1] This is not apparently true in all sections of the country. In some jurisdictions physicians can perform "limited autopsies," exploring only those areas of the body which are believed to be directly associated with the death, without obtaining permission from the family. See, for example, S. Cutolo, *Bellevue Is My Home* (Garden City: Doubleday & Company, Inc., 1956), p. 155. In those cases in which the coroner's office is involved in a death, no autopsy permission need be obtained.

The autopsy permit reads:

I _____ bearing the relation of _____ to _____, a patient recently deceased in County Hospital, authorize the proper authorities to
examine the body and head of said deceased patient and to remove
organs and to retain such portions as may be considered necessary for
further study to ascertain the correct cause of death.

Signed _____

Nearest Relative

2

The autopsy percentage of hospital deaths reflects the degree of ex-
cellence of the medical staff. Institutions which conduct intern and
resident programs should obtain an autopsy rate of 25 percent as a
minimum. The average good general hospital should aim for a minimum of 50 percent, though some outstanding institutions obtain percentages of 70 or higher.

J. K. Owen, *Modern Concepts of Hospital Administration* (Philadelphia: W. B. Saunders Co., 1962), p. 304. It is to be noted that
physicians have a vested interest in the overall death rate. A hospital
where few patients die is less suitable for training, whatever the percentage of autopsies. It is a high percentage of a large number of cases,
providing many autopsy possibilities, which is desired. With every
death, it is claimed, more experience is gained.

[3] In some hospitals, however, obtaining pre-death autopsy permits
is openly encouraged, as for example at Cook County:

One of the most important characteristics of a well regulated hospital
is that it obtains as many autopsies as possible. For this the hospital
depends to the largest degree on the residents and interns of the ward.
They must recognize cases in which death is imminent or likely, and
must make an immediate effort to advise the nearest of kin of the seriousness of the case, and to request written permit of autopsy. They
must use their ingenuity in acquainting the relative with the importance
of the autopsy. . . . Often in hopeless cases, the intern can succeed in
obtaining a permit for a limited autopsy if he can show that it is not
more than an operation.

A. Bernstein, *Intern's Manual (Cook County Hospital)* (Chicago:
Year Book Medical Publishers, Inc., 1959), p. 190.

[4] M. MacEachern, *Hospital Organization and Management,* 3rd
Edition (Chicago: Physicians Record Company, 1957), the standard
source book on hospital administrative policy, gives the following as
a "standing order":

Care of the Body after Death
Wash the body carefully, plug the rectum (male) and vagina (female) with cotton, tie the chin so that the mouth is closed, close the eyes, dress the body in its clothes if these are available, and if not wrap the body in a morgue sheet. A morgue basket is to be found in the central supply room.

A thirty-four item list of steps in the wrapping of a body is given in G. Cherescavich, *A Textbook for Nursing Assistants* (St. Louis: The C. V. Mosby Co., 1964), 455-457.

[5] This annoyance has been noted by other observers. For example, K. R. Eissler, *The Psychiatrist and the Dying Patient,* (New York: International Universities Press, Inc., 1955), p. 42, notes:

> . . . I have noticed in a few instances that dying may be conceived of as a malicious act performed for the sake of annoying others. One physician complained bitterly that most of his fatal patients died at night and that he had to get up to sign their death certificates. There was no doubt that he had the fantasy that patients could have died at a different time had they not meant to annoy him.

[6] For a discussion of "non-person" treatment see E. Goffman, *Presentation of Self in Everyday Life* (Garden City: Doubleday & Company, Inc., 1959), pp. 151-152.

[7] Formally, at least, nurses are instructed in textbooks:

> Nothing should be said in the room that he should not hear, for no one knows how much the seemingly unconscious person can hear. Whispering especially should be avoided. The patient may see the lips move and be distressed that he cannot hear what is said.

B. Harmer, *Textbook of the Principles and Practice of Nursing,* 5th edition (New York: The MacMillan Company, 1955), p. 933. See also, E. Meyers, "Nursing the Comatose Patient," *American Journal of Nursing,* 54, 716-718.

[8]

> . . . the classical deathbed scene, with its loving partings and solemn last words, is practically a thing of the past; in its stead is a sedated, comatose, betubed object, manipulated and subconscious, if not sub-human.

From J. Fletcher, "The Patient's Right to Die," *Harper's,* 221 (October, 1960), p. 141.

It is to be noted that the "Hollywood version," as a production, can be reproduced in actual circumstances, despite the comatose situation, when persons are assembled at the bedside to await the final breath. The absence of this sort of scene can be regarded, partially at least, as a consequence of the lack of such production as much as a consequence of the way "death occurs." It is interesting that arguments for euthanasia rest heavily upon claiming that mercy killing will end the life of a "vegetable," which, it is argued, does not seem worth preserving. If one regards that "vegetable" life as a consequence of social arrangements (and, perhaps, the use of heavy sedations in the first place), then it would seem equally plausible to suggest that rather than euthanasia, what is needed is to let the death be the death of a live man and not a vegetable. Those who propose the "honorable death" supposedly have this alternative in mind, as Orwell, who says it is best not to die in a hospital at all. The "need" for euthanasia seems to be a direct consequence of the patterns of care and regard for pain which modern medical practice has institutionalized. L. Wertenbaker's *Death of a Man* (London: William Heinemann, Limited, 1957), portrays a vivid example of a man who refused to be placed in a position where euthanasia might be a relevant consideration by fighting his cancer to its end outside of the hospital.

[9] For discussions of the timing of prognostications in other settings, see F. Davis, "Uncertainty in Medical Prognosis," *American Journal of Sociology*, July, 1960, pp. 41-47, and J. Roth, *Timetables* (Indianapolis: The Bobbs-Merrill Co., Inc., 1963), Chapters I and II. For a discussion of the tenuous position of the physician at the time of death, see W. L. Warner, *The Living and the Dead* (New Haven: Yale University Press, 1959), pp. 310-314.

[10] There is a large literature on the subject of euthanasia, most of which treats inherent definitional difficulties. See particularly, G. Williams, *The Sanctity of Life and the Criminal Law* (New York: Alfred A. Knopf, Inc., 1957), pp. 311-350, J. Fletcher, *Morale and Medicine* (Princeton: Princeton University Press, 1954), pp. 178-190, and N. St. John-Stevas, *Life, Death and the Law* (New York: Meridian Books, 1961), Chapter 7, pp. 262-281.

V. *Death, Uses of a Corpse, and Social Worth*

[1] There is a large popular and scientific literature developing on efforts to "treat the dead," the import of which is to undercut traditional notions of the non-reversibility of death. Some of this discussion goes so far as to propose the preservation of corpses in a state of nondeterioration until such time as medical science will be able to do complete renovative work. See particularly R. Ettinger, *The Prospect of Immortality* (Garden City: Doubleday & Company, Inc., 1964). The Soviet literature on resuscitation is most extensive. Soviet physicians have given far more attention to this problem than any others in the world. For an extensive review of the technical literature, as well as a discussion of bio-medical principles, with particular emphasis on cardiac arrest, see V. A. Negovskii, *Resuscitation and Artificial Hypothermia* (New York: Consultants Bureau Enterprises Inc., 1962). See also, L. Fridland, *The Achievement of Soviet Medicine* (New York: Twayne Publishers, Inc., 1961), especially Chapter Two, "Death Deceived," pp. 56-75. For an account of the famous saving of the Soviet physicist Landau's life, see A. Dorozynski, *The Man They Wouldn't Let Die* (New York: The Macmillan Company, 1956).

For recent popular articles on "bringing back the dead" and treating death as a reversible process, see "The Reversal of Death," *The Saturday Review,* August 4, 1962; "A New Fight Against Sudden Death," *Look,* December 1, 1964.

Soviet efforts and conceptions of death as reversible might be seen to have their ideological basis in principles of dialectics:

> For everyday purposes we know and can say, e.g., whether an animal is alive or not. But, upon closer inquiry, we find that this is, in many cases a very complex question, as the jurists know very well. They have cudgelled their brains in vain to discover a rational limit beyond which the killing of the child in its mother's womb is murder. It is just as impossible to determine absolutely the moment of death, for physiology provides that death is not an instantaneous, momentary phenomenon, but a very protracted process.
>
> In like manner, every organized being is every moment the same and not the same . . .

From F. Engels, *Socialism: Utopian and Scientific* (New York: International Publishers Co., Inc., 1935), p. 47.

For a discussion of primitive conceptions of death with particular attention to the passage between life and death, see I. A. Lopatin, *The Cult of the Dead Among the Natives of the Amur Basin* (The Hague: Mouton and Company, 1960), pp. 26-27 and 39-41.

[2] The "DOA" deaths of famous persons are reportedly attended with considerably prolonged and intensive resuscitation efforts. In Kennedy's death, for example, it was reported:

> Medically, it was apparent the President was not alive when he was brought in. There was no spontaneous respiration. He had dilated, fixed pupils. It was obviously a lethal head wound.
>
> Technically, however, by using vigorous resuscitation, intraveneous tubes and all the usual supportive measures, we were able to raise the semblance of a heart beat.

The New York Times, November 23, 1963, p. 2.

VII. *Bad News*

[1] By such a listing I do not intend to suggest that there is not a much wider variety of matters about which obligation is felt that they be reported upon, so that, for example, the nurse will feel responsible for relaying a message from a patient to a member of his family. I intend to restrict attention to those events which have a clearly perceived announcement type structure, events with presentational formats such as, "I have something to tell you."

[2] There is a key exception which occurs when such news is purposefully withheld from someone because it is presumed likely to be detrimental to his health. In County Hospital, at least, the decision as to whether or not to so withhold news was not felt to be the physician's. Doctors would only avoid relating news if they were advised to do so by other members of the family.

[3] This practice seems generally related to the difficulty persons have in greeting one another from a distance, e.g., when walking toward each other from opposite directions on a sidewalk, when meeting someone at an airplane, etc. Persons seem unable to maintain continuous eye contact in such approach situations without experiencing some uneasiness, and there is usually the sense of incompleteness, wherein an initial greeting is suspended until persons get close enough to follow through the greeting with a more complete sequence. In situ-

ations of bad news, the deliverer seeks to rapidly shorten this distance, so as to get close enough for his eyes to convey the seriousness of what is to follow and hence the need to inhibit any typical sociable greeting extension before it gets under way.

[4] It is to be pointed out that when body identification is requested, as is done in the coroner's office, that identification is generally not a precondition for notifying others of that person's death, nor is identification employed as the means of notification. In the greatest number of "identifications," the coroner reported, persons are not told "would you come to the coroner's office to identify a body," or "we think your wife died and we want you to come to identify this body and see if it is your wife." Rather, I was told, the identification of bodies is put as a legally required formality, and officials will not qualify their announcements of death pending that legal identification. In the greatest number of coroner cases bereavement has already begun before the relative comes to the county morgue to make the identification.

[5] There is a common form of "disbelief" which purportedly occurs with some frequency among bereaved persons. Bereaved persons have been reported to go through periods where they engage in conversations with their deceased relatives, set the dinner table for them, and otherwise refuse to "accept" the fact of the death. These clinical varieties of disbelief were not observed in the reactions to the news of death in the hospital. Whatever might have been the later cognitive orientations of relatives with respect to the death's occurrence, in the hospital no expressions of disbelief of this radical character were observed. Such forms of disbelief are to be distinguished from expressions of incredulity, which were very common, e.g., "I just can't believe it," "it doesn't seem real," "he was so young it just doesn't make sense," etc.

[6] A comment about the sociological analysis of grieving behavior seems warranted. There has been a tendency in the (limited) sociological literature on grief to place a one-sided emphasis on the role of normative elements in expressive behavior. Durkheim's classic statement sets the tone for this emphasis:

> . . . mourning is not a natural movement of private feelings wounded by cruel loss; it is a duty imposed by the group. One weeps, not simply because he is sad, but because he is forced to weep. It is a ritual attitude which he is forced to adopt . . . but which is, in a large measure,

independent of his affective state. E. Durkheim, *Elementary Forms of Religious Life* (New York: The Free Press, of Glencoe, Inc., 1947), p. 397.

It can be warrantably said, I believe, that a vulgar, not uncommon reading of Durkheim readily implies a debunking, degrading, and discrediting view of the bereaved person. Despite Durkheim's weak reservation "not simply because he is sad," the dominant tone of the "normative" perspective, improperly implied in this and other analyses, can be extended as follows: "people cry because it is expected of them that they cry; they are not really as upset or disoriented as their behavior would imply; people are basically fakes in a normative order." It is not a far step, given an emphasis which one-sidedly says: persons' actual emotions are probably less severe than the normatively appropriate mode of expression requires, to debunking bereaved persons and eliminating the possibility of "genuine grief."

While I am by no means suggesting suspension of interest in normatively prescribed expressive modes, nor a generalized humanist stance, I am proposing that a more sophisticated mode of analysis is to be required if one wishes to assess the actual operation of "expectations." Consider the following possibility (which I believe to be frequently the case): persons express considerably less grief than they actually experience, particularly in semi-public encounters with relative strangers like the hospital physician, and for that matter, at a funeral, for prescribed and available cultural models for appropriate expressiveness may be severely limiting, requiring a through and through curtailment on actually experienced feelings of loss. So that the relative might say of the relation between the appearance he is presenting and the grief he "actually feels": it is impossible for you to know what it is like; I'm crying all right but you can't imagine how little that says about my feelings.

Fortunately, Durkheim's statement, properly read, need not be simplistically and discreditingly applied, but, in its general terms, permits of any of a wide range of possible interpretations of the relationship between presented appearances and underlying sentiment. Persons who are apparently obliging an order of crying in the hospital or walking down the street, can be viewed as in fact standing in any of a variety of relations to the apparentness of their activities, e.g., one of cynicism, sarcasm, mocking, feigning, underplaying, dramatizing, etc. They can be viewed, when composed, as merely obliging the requirements for demonstrating upsettedness, upset to a degree commensurate with what appears, or upset far in excess of their apparent display of grief.

It is a central feature of bereavement situations that the rule-governed character of expressive behavior is precisely its most problematic aspect. In the routinization of contacts between bereaved and non-bereaved persons we see continuous work involved in the adjustment of actual feelings to the conditions of concrete interactional situations, wherein there is both a considerable amount of underplaying and overplaying of expressive demonstration, required to handle the conditions of interaction between parties holding varying perspectives toward the death. The fact that knowledge and use of the proprieties becomes problematic for bereaved and non-bereaved has its basis in the fact that the temporally graded social definitions of the status "bereaved" establish conditions of ambiguity. A view of bereavement behavior adequate to description of the circumstances grieving entails in the case of a society in which a whole range of contacts occur, from those involving the most intimate of relations to those involving the mere acquainted, must treat the essentially troublesome character of the normative elements in grief. Persons are engaged, so it seems, in the continual de-emphasis of their feelings of loss, out of respect for the difficulties of interaction facing those less intimately involved in the death than themselves. It is such de-emphasis, the underlying obligations for which concern the requirements of ordinary conversational discourse, that available notions of grieving as "culturally appropriate" fail to handle, for such notions ignore the situational and interactional determinants of the limits of grieving behavior.

[7] The political scientist Oakeshott's analysis of conversation so nicely describes the general character I found to the talk in these settings that it deserves a lengthy citation:

> In a conversation, the participants are not engaged in an enquiry or a debate; there is no "truth" to be discovered, no proposition to be proved, no conclusion sought. They are not concerned to inform, to persuade, or to refute one another, and therefore the cogency of their utterances does not depend upon their all speaking in the same idiom; they may differ without disagreeing . . . In conversation, "facts" appear only to be resolved once more into the possibilities from which they were made; "certainties" are shown to be combustible, not by

being brought in contact with other "certainties" or with doubts, but by being kindled by the presence of ideas of another order; approximations are revealed between notions normally remote from one another. Thoughts of different species take wing and play round one another, responding to each other's movements and provoking one another to fresh exertions. Nobody asks where they have come from or on what authority they are present; nobody cares what will become of them when they have played their part. There is no symposiarch or arbiter; not even a doorkeeper to examine credentials. Every entrant is taken at its face-value and everything is permitted which can get itself ac-caccepted into the flow of speculation. And voices which speak in conversation do not compose a hierarchy. Conversation is not an enterprise designed to yield an extrinsic profit, a contest where a winner gets a prize, nor is it an activity of exegesis; it is an unrehearsed intellectual adventure.

M. Oakshott, *The Voice of Poetry in the Conversation of Mankind* (London: Bowes and Bowes, 1959), pp. 10-11.

Oakeshott's analysis, so reminiscent of Simmel's brilliant essay on the structure of sociability, elucidates that key feature of "mere talk," its production in accord, first and foremost, with respect to the conventions of ordinary polite interchange, wherein the topic becomes the vehicle of expression and not the matter of predominant interest.

It is to be noted, of course, that insofar as there is a clear restriction of topic here to the occurrence of the death, such sociability as may be discovered in this occasion differs somewhat from pure form sociability, described by Simmel. While Simmel clearly saw the elemental character of conversation as that basic of social activities, his analysis was rather more restricted to the "party," wherein content shifts regularly and requiredly, and the play of "forms" has an essentially artful character. See K. Wolff, ed., *The Sociology of Georg Simmel,* (New York: Free Press of Glencoe, Ill., 1950), pp. 40-57.

[8] L. Tolstoy, *War and Peace,* (New York: Modern Library, n.d.), p. 1.

[9] *Ibid.,* p. 704.

Appendix I

"DYING" AS A SOCIAL FACT

That a person is "dying" is not an altogether straightforward notion, given the possibility that it can properly be said of all persons, in a manner of speaking, that from the moment of birth they move closer to death each day and are, in that sense, continually and forever "dying." This recognition is, of course, at the time both a major resource and dilemma of existential philosophy and literature.

Despite the awareness of continual "dying-from-birth," considered by some as the most profound awareness of man, people in Western society, at least, do not ordinarily employ "dying" but with respect to a rather delimited class of states and persons, and in so doing, seem to confront no great philosophical conflict in saying of that one: "he is dying," yet not admitting the same fact of themselves. It is the more mundane, ordinary use of the characterization whose analysis is of direct relevance to my concerns. While perhaps philosophically admissible as a description of whomsoever, the notion "dying" has a strictly circumscribed domain of proper use in the hospital setting. I should like to propose an empirical description of this use, as well as the assessment "he is dead," it too being a somewhat problematic notion.[1]

---

[1] By conceiving of these categories as "problematic" I do not intend at all to suggest that their use is problematic for either professional or lay persons, but rather that, from the sociologist's standpoint, they must be so conceived if the proper analytic attitude toward them is to be maintained. I intend the term "problematic" in accord with Harold Garfinkel's usage, as for example in his "Studies in the Routine Grounds of Everyday Activities," *Social Problems,* Volume II (Winter, 1964), pp. 235-250.

It is to be noted from the outset that the characterizations "he is dead" and "he is dying" (as well as their chief lexical variants in the hospital setting: "he is deceased" and "he is terminally ill"), are the products of assessment procedures, constituting the outcomes of investigative inquiries of more or less detail, undertaken by persons more or less practically involved in the consequences which discovery of those outcomes foreseeably have. To be "dead" or "dying" is, from our sociological perspective, to be so regarded by those who routinely and rightfully engage in assessing those states and premising courses of action, both for themselves and others, on the basis of these assessments. An interest we take in these phenomena is directed towards explicating how these assessments are made and reported upon within the organizational milieu of the hospital social system.

It is perhaps not altogether impossible to conceive of the circumstance where "dying" was not a matter which persons attended to, where persons simply died, for varieties of reasons, and where, at the time of the death it would be regarded as strange to be asked to retrospectively locate that point at which "dying" could be said to have begun. The philosophic recognition that "dying" begins when life does, might seem to make such a location attempt quite arbitrary, if not meaningless.

Yet deaths occur in a social order. The thoughts, concerns, activities, projects, prospects and fate of others are more or less linked to the one who dies and the fact of his death. The character of this linkage is partially given by the location of the person in a variety of social structures: the family, the hospital, the occupationally structured careers of the society, the age-graded system. These social structures provide, in turn, for the varying degrees of relevance of anticipating death and programming courses of action on the basis of such an anticipation. Death occurs in an organizational-based medical order as well. The programming of courses of treatment, the activities of diagnosis and prognosis, the appropriation of time, interest and money are among the practical and sanctionable concerns of the medical professionals, and the anticipation of persons' deaths figures prominently into the way such concerns are concretely organized.[2]

2 Of relevance here is Glaser and Strauss, *op. cit.*, and their "Awareness Contexts and Social Interaction," *American Sociological Review*, Volume XXIX, October, 1964, pp. 669-678. See also their book, *Awareness of Dying*, *op. cit.* A key difference between my approach and theirs, is that in their

"Dying" comes to be noticed at certain points and not others in the course of a life, despite the existential proposition of dying-from-birth, and whatever the medical basis of its proper recognition (and that perhaps is problematic), there are many respects in which the most criterial features of the notion's use have to do with explicitly social considerations.

The medical, biological or physio-chemical basis for regarding a person as "dying" is not entirely clear. Noticing "dying" seems to be a quite different order of conceptual activity than noticing bleeding, fibrilating or employing a disease category to organize some set of

---

analysis, what "dying" consists of is not treated as a problematic phenomenon. Their central interest, of considerable social-psychological importance, is the management of information in interaction; their central issue is "awareness of dying" and for their purposes what "dying" is has not been accorded central attention. I have found it necessary, being less concerned with interaction between staff and patient and more concerned with the organization of ward activities, to regard the very phenomenon of "dying" as troublesome, an understanding of its sense requiring location of those practices which its use warrants.

Generally, I have not considered the "patient's knowledge" of his own likely forthcoming death, a topic of considerable interest and one which Glaser and Strauss treat in detail. Only infrequently in my observations at County did I encounter conversations between staff and patients about forthcoming death, or among staff about patients' awarenesses. The deaths I witnessed seldom involved a patient whose condition was such that interaction with him was likely. It is my feeling that a considerable number of deaths involve the circumstance where awareness of "dying" is irrelevant, from an organizational perspective, with a chief exception being cancer, where both patients and staff members are involved in daily social interaction. Deaths of patients suffering from heart disease, kidney disease, CVA's (strokes) and liver diseases have a course such that at that point when "dying" becomes noticeable, during the patient's "last admission" to the hospital, the patient is, so to speak, out of the picture. The greatest "cause of death," heart disease, typically "produces" death in the course of a short term hospital admission, eventuating from an "attack" and is not preceded by that lengthy period of consciousness which is the fate of the cancer victim.

For other discussions of "awareness" see, Standard, S., and Nathan, H., *Should the Patient Know the Truth?* (New York: Springer Publishing Company), 1955; Kelly, W. D., and Friesen, S. R., "Do Cancer Patients Want to be Told?", *Surgery*, Volume 27, p. 822, 1950; Field, M., *Patients Are People* (New York: Columbia University Press), 1953, pp. 72-76.

symptoms and findings. As a "medical category," "dying" seems clearly distinguished from disease categories on one hand and bio-chemico-physical states and processes on the other. "Dying" does not, in the American system of medicine, at least, stand as an appropriate answer to questions on the order of "What's wrong with me, Doc-tor?" which questions seem partially definitive of "diseases." "Dis-eases" can be said to consist of those linguistic items which can properly be taken to stand as answers to questions taking this form. "Dying" does not properly stand as such an answer.[3]

The question "What's wrong with me?" does not always elicit a disease category as an answer but does, on occasion, elicit an enumera-tion of some set of symptoms, purported happenings or conditions. So the question "What's wrong with him?" may elicit, as proper re-sponses, "He has X," "He complains of X," "He is X-ing," and, of course, variations on "I don't know." The elements of enumerations, when they are given, may or may not be organizable into some disease category or categories. "Dying" however, is not an appropriate descrip-tive term in such enumerations as they occur in our society generally and in the medical world specifically.

"Dying" seems to be an essentially predictive term. It appears to be the case that when nurses in the hospital say "You can tell that some-one is dying just by looking at them," what they are pointing to is that given some set of observable happenings, known about happenings or assumed happenings death is likely to occur in such and such a period of time. Seeing "dying" is seeing the likelihood of death within some temporal perspective. It is not like seeing cancer, shock or bleed-ing. In the medical world one learns to see dying when, in the course of his experience with critically ill persons, he can learn to detect signs which warrant a particular order of time-specific death predic-tions.

What the existential proposition of "dying"-from-birth may perhaps provide is an extended temporal perspective based on the recognition of man's mortality. The actuarial table provides a more specified age-

[3] This conception of "disease categories" is taken from the excellent paper by Charles Frake, "The Diagnosis of Disease Among the Subanun of Mindanao," *American Anthropologist,* Volume 63, 1961, pp. 113-132.

graded system of temporal reference brackets in terms of which "death" can be statistically predicted; disease categories, symptoms and biochemical happenings, the data and conceptual apparatus of medicine provide a still more specified temporal perspective. So the existentialist can, in his philosophical moments, regard the newborn baby (or yet-to-be-born fetus) as "dying"; and the insurance salesman, in his calculation of premium rates, the likelihood of "deaths" within varying specifiable times, with varying degrees of predictive accuracy; and the physician or nurse, or otherwise knowledgeable person in matters of illness, the likelihood of "death" given X and Y symptoms, or happenings, or diseases.

What the medical perspective on life provides, via the use of diseases and biological events generally as prognosticators, is another among a variety of possible timetables in terms of which predictions of "death," or talk of "dying" is framed. In our society, at least, medical people seem to have obtained a franchise on the notion of "dying," despite the philosopher's existential recognition and the insurance man's predictive tables. If one seeks to know if he is "dying" he consults his physician, not his insurance broker. There appears to be some special power to the notion of "fatal illness," such that the philosopher's description of "life as a fatal illness" does not constitute a threat, but the doctor's discovery of a cancer does. Wherein that special power lies is a matter of some interest; first, the notion of the "fatal illness" requires comment.

To say of a person that he "died from cancer" is, in some circles (that of medical pathologists), a somewhat strange way of talking.[4] The actual occurrence of a death involves the operation of a rather specific set of mechanisms, none of which are currently understood in great detail, and none of which are specifically included under the general rubric cancer, neither as its definitive features, nor as cancer's

[4] See Pearl, R., *The Biology of Death* (Philadelphia: J. B. Lippincott), 1922, particularly pp. 102-110, and Riese, W., *The Conception of Disease* (New York: Philosophical Library), 1953. When pathologists give reports on the cause of death in the course of hospital "death rounds" their descriptions generally make no mention of a "disease," but rather, a detailed tracing of lesions and a sequential account of the progressive destruction of cellular tissue is provided.

specific inevitable consequences. To "die," some say, the heart must cease beating, and that can occur as a direct result of one or more of a series of quite specific bio-chemico-physical occurrences; the heart can burst open in certain instances of trauma, the nerve tissue which provides the heart with its electrical stimulation can be damaged, or weakened through a loss of blood supply. Yet cessation of the heart is currently considered by some to be merely a "sign" of death, and not definitive of it. In certain medical circles there is considerable disagreement over the precise biological meaning of death. Some argue that the cessation of cellular activity constitutes death, others insist upon a more specific attention to properties of cellular multiplication. All generally agree that the definition of "death" that will be most satisfactory will be one based on an understanding of "life's specific mechanisms" and not "disease categories," which can be regarded as only "predisposing conditions." As predisposing conditions some of the so-called "fatal illnesses" constitute good predictors of death. Their located presence warrants making a prediction of death within limits which could not be specified without their location.

Some persons argue that "dying" is a thing which becomes recognizeable once such a deadly disease is located, that "dying" is a state wherein a person suffers from a disease which is nonreversible and known to "produce death." For purposes of setting up the features of my argument, let me examine this position from a somewhat critical perspective. An argument with lay conceptions is not intended. My concern in regarding them critically is to eventually focus in on their definitive features.

On one count, location of a "death-causing disease" does not warrant talk of "dying," namely, that that talk occurs when a disease of this character cannot be located, i.e., when certain symptoms, biological events, or conditions are noticed but where the organization of those matters into a disease category cannot, for a variety of reasons, be successfully achieved. The patient who arrives in the Emergency Ward of County, in a state of deep "shock," may be considered "dying," even though no disease has been cited as a description or causal account of his condition. The disease may be discovered retrospectively, at an autopsy, or there may be no disease whatever, the death being described as due to some traumatic occurrence.

On another count, the location of a "death-causing disease" does not warrant talk of "dying," namely, that the present set of diseases do not, in any strict sense, stand as adequate causal accounts of death. On still a third count, the location of a "death-causing disease" does not exclusively warrant talk and treatment of a person as "dying," for persons with such diseases are not always so regarded. In the hospital setting, the eighty-five year old man with advanced arteriosclerosis will not always, on the basis of the disease itself, be regarded as a "dying man."

In nearly every hospital in the United States there is a book which one will find at nurses' stations, on doctors' desks, and in the hospital morgue. It contains a lengthy list of items headed "causes of death," any one of which can be properly entered in the legal death certificate where the "cause of death" is requested.[5] In addition to disease categories, like "carcinoma of the stomach" and "myocardial infarction," there are certain physical occurrences which are considered "nonnatural," like "poisoning," "drowning," "natural amputation." These "causes of death" consist of those diseases and physical occurrences which are legally taken as sufficient explanations of the death. They stand as legitimate, adequate answers to the question: "Why did he die?" They are used as answers for recording on the death certificate, for telling members of the deceased's family why he died, for satisfying insurance requirements for a "natural death." Their adequacy as accounts is a legal and socially given adequacy and not a biochemically descriptive adequacy.

The collection of diseases, including the so-called fatal illnesses, which medicine, at any point in its development, employs in organizing treatment, teaching its students and filling out death certificates are products of the current state of medical knowledge. As that knowledge changes, the culturally defined collection of disease categories becomes more elaborate. Diseases which were previously considered independent of one another come to be recognized, under the auspices of new principles of organizing biochemical facts, as related in formerly unrecognized ways. Diseases which were earlier thought to be varieties of some more generic diseases, come to be regarded as worthy of inde-

[5] American Medical Association, *Standard Nomenclature of Diseases and Operations,* (Philadelphia: Blakiston), Fourth edition, 1952.

pendent status as distinctive entities and new diseases are discovered.[6] That *cancer* is now regarded as a "fatal illness" and a prevalent "cause of death" is a function of the direction which medical inquiry currently takes. It is conceivable (and indeed a goal of researchers in this field) that as cancer's mechanisms are better understood, the antecedents of cancer will become more precisely locatable, so that one may detect this "fatal illness" in its pre-symptomatic stages, perhaps to the extent that a new order of phenomenon, having to do with the multiplying propensities of certain cellular structures, becomes designated as the "fatal illness." In some important senses, it can be said that the goal of medical research is to locate the fatal illnesses we all contain within us—a principled medical description of "life as a fatal illness."

The point of the above paragraphs is to suggest that currently available and employed categories of diseases, as sanctionably used "causes of death" are culturally constituted entities, and that death is an "outcome" of "diseases" in a socially accepted manner of speaking, but not in any strict biochemical sense.[7] What seems to set off some cancer patients from the "well," or at least some cancer patients, is not simply that they have a "fatal disease which will kill them," for it can be said of all of us that we have "fatal diseases in progress," which will

[6] For discussions of the changing character of disease categories see Dubos, R., *Mirage of Health,* (Garden City, N.Y.: Doubleday Anchor), 1961, especially Chapters IV and VI; Sigarest, H. E., *A History of Medicine,* (New York: Oxford University Press), 2 volumes, 1951; and Sir James Spence, "The Methodology of the Clinical Sciences," in *Lectures on the Scientific Basis of Medicine,* (London: Athlono Press), Volume II, 1952-53, pp. 1-14.

A listing of "causes of death" in 1736 in London, included "apoplexy," "old age," "lunacy," and "jaundice." "Old age" was the largest "killer." See *The Gentleman's Magazine and the London Bill of Mortality, 1731-1778* (New Jersey: Ross Paxton), 1963, p. 24.

[7] The juxtaposition of "biochemical" and "social" is here intended merely for the sake of my argument, which is, in fact, that such distinctions are not necessarily viable. As is the case with the concepts death and dying so it is expectably the case with other hard and fast natural dichotomies, namely, that they are through and through socially constituted. The very biologic determination of death, as a judgmental activity performed by actors in an organizational environment, can be seen as itself a socially prescribed activity. For a brilliant analysis of sexual status which treats the issue of "natural" facts of life in detail, see Garfinkel, H., "Passing and the Management of Achieved Sexual Status in an Intersexed Person," U.C.L.A., mimeographed.

kill us, and these could be located (and perhaps will be) were it not
for the particular diagnostic direction medical inquiry currently takes
and the current state of medical knowledge. A partially distinguishing
fact about the cancer patient, is the degree of accuracy with which
predictions of his death within some specifiable time period can be
made by virtue of the detected presence of a cancerous growth. This
predictive accuracy is the result of extensive research in developing
prognostic indicators and fatality tables for the disease *cancer*. It is
to be noted, of course, that actuarial tables provide a reasonably accurate basis for temporally specifying predictions of death. For example,
the eighty year old, with no locatable disease of a "fatal" character,
can be statistically predicted to die within a short time period and
with as much predictive accuracy as the person with a newly developed
cancer.

Yet such an eighty year old will not, in our society, always be conceived as "dying," nor in the hospital as a "terminal patient." If predictive accuracy in foreseeing death within specific time periods and
the location of a so-called "fatal illness" are not, in themselves, sufficient conditions for conceiving of a person as "dying," then what is?
The eighty year old who develops carcinoma of the stomach will not
always be regarded as "dying," yet the twenty year old who develops
Hodgkin's Disease often will be.

The answer seems to lie in the way temporal specification of a prediction of forthcoming death is linked to the person's location along
the temporal dimensions of a variety of social structures, and the way
temporal specifications of predictions of death involve those who make
them in a variety of organizational, interactional and professional
problems. I shall consider each of these forms of linkage in turn, and
argue that an understanding of them is required to adequately grasp
what the notion of "dying" means within the hospital context.

That a twenty year old will expectably die in ten years is, in our
society, an apparently more relevant fact than that a seventy-five year
old has an expectably similar length of time to live before his death,
and that relevance has to do, it seems with each's respective place in
a variety of social structures. "Dying" becomes an important, noticeable "process" insofar as it serves to provide others, as well as the patient, with a way to orient to a future, organize activities around the
expectability of death and to "prepare for it." The notion of "dying"

appears to be a distinctly social one, for its central relevance is provided
for by the fact that it establishes a way of attending a person. Physicians and nurses don't treat "dying," but diseases, symptoms and happenings; yet they seem to have a special way of regarding and caring
for persons once they come to conceive of them as "dying." In the hospital, as elsewhere, what the notion of "dying" does, as a predictive
characterization, is place a cognitive frame of interpretation around a
person.

In the County hospital setting, over 75 percent of the patients are
over sixty years of age. The mere location of a "fatal illness" does not,
for hospital personnel, warrant employing "dying," or "terminality,"
in any special sense. Many of County's patients have locatable "fatal
illnesses, illnesses which, should the person die, could be appropriately
entered on a death certificate as the "cause of death." The patient
population includes many persons with advanced carcinomas, arterio-
sclerotic heart disease, severe liver and kidney malfunctioning.

Generally and ideally, for persons so located in the age structure of
the society, the fact of their eventual and perhaps shortly upcoming
deaths is attended by family members. The social structures in which
they are involved are oriented to the fact of their forthcoming death.
Their families have become increasingly independent of them, and the
scope of references to the "future" has progressively narrowed; their
careers are regarded retrospectively and not prospectively.[8] It is considered proper to treat the "fact" of their "dying" as of considerable
less consequence for others, and it is not felt to be a matter which
requires drastic revision of others' life plans, as does the "fact" that a
young adult is "dying."

Physicians, in treating and attending their elderly patients, do not
regard the fact of "death within ten years" as warranting any special
consideration although this is a very basic one as regards the way the
whole structure of medical practice with the elderly is organized. In
dealing with elderly patients, there need be no conscious avoidance of

[8] For a general discussion of the disengagement of the elderly from on-
going social life, see Cumming, E., and Henry, W., *Growing Old,* (New
York: Basic Books), 1961, especially Chapter XII. For an extended treat-
ment of the place of the elderly in nonWestern societies, see, Simmons, L.,
The Role of the Aged in Primitive Societies, (New Haven: Yale University
Press), 1945.

future references, as is characteristically the case in conversing with the young adult who is expected to die within an abnormally short time period. In our society, such references are systematically and "naturally" dropped from conversation with the aged. A most noticeable fact about interaction between medical personnel and young "dying" patients is the careful avoidance of long-term future references. A nurse reported her trouble in talking to a young teenager who was "dying" of Hodgkin's Disease and knew her life span was expectably short. The greatest problem she experienced was to keep from talking about plans for school, a marriage, a career. In conversing with the elderly, the future becomes attended as the days and the weeks to follow. For the older patient, "dying" comes to mean, for hospital personnel, *dying on this admission to the hospital.* That the patient may die within the year or the month becomes, within the hospital context at least, a manageable possibility so long as the patient is old; such a possibility requires no special daily interactional contortions, no planned avoidance of death and the future as conversational topics.

With the young person, noticing "dying" is a crucial matter as regards certain interactional problems. A young teenager at County had moderately advanced leukemia, a disease which often does not seriously debilitate its victim until its very late stages. She came to County during the critical phases of her illness; in the course of several years she was purportedly in and out of the hospital dozens of times, a characteristic hospital career pattern for patients with this disease. This girl was in the ambulatory section of the female medical ward and spent most of her days in the hospital walking up and down the corridors. A new member of the nursing staff engaged her in conversation on the first day of a new admission, and asked her, while talking about those things which one talks with teenage girls about: "Do you have a boyfriend," "When do you want to get married?" The girl, who was said to be "very mature" in her attitude toward her illness, interrupted the nurse with the announcement: "I'm going to die in a few years and have learned not to think about such things." The nurse was visibly upset by the fact that she had unwittingly led the conversation in such directions; other nurses apologized for not having told her about the facts of the case.

Few such cases are available from my data at County, where the

average age of the patient population is well over 50.[9] In the local
area there are several specialized children's hospital and teaching hospitals which accept "charity cases," so that County treats very few
young, "dying" patients. Of the some 250 deaths on which my observations are based, only a handful involved persons under forty years
of age.

With the average County patients, the danger of unwittingly entering conversation inappropriate with a "dying" patient is relatively
nonexistent. Few of the hospital's patients are in any condition for
sociable interaction, and more importantly, conversation with the
"dying" (in County the elderly) need not be specially modified insofar
as the things one normally discusses with them are not premised on,
or take their meaning from, any understanding of a long-term future.
At County, "dying" shifts in importance from a fact whose notice is
of great relevance as a basis of attending the younger person within a
long-term temporal perspective, e.g., in terms of a career, family, etc.,
to a fact whose relevance, with the elderly, is great only if death is
considered an imminent possibility. For hospital personnel, the domain
of relevant considerations is the hospital organization and the activities that go on within it. "Dying" takes its central sense against the
background of these activities. The older the patient, the more readily
hospital personnel can naturally attend the expectation of death within
years, and restrict the sense of "dying," to "dying this time."

There are, of course, exceptions to the general tendency for "dying"
to become restricted in temporal reference and significance with age.
The most notable instances are those where the person whose death is
contemplated occupies some special place in the wider social structure.
That an elder statesman is expected to die within the term of his
office, can become a quite serious matter to attend. "Dying," in the
case of an elderly man, can be of utmost importance to an heir-to-be

[9] Glaser and Strauss, "Awareness Contexts and Social Interaction," *op.
cit.*, pp. 55-56, locate the control of future references in the degree of awareness staff have of the patients' conditions. While that is certainly an important determinant, as is seen in the above cited example, my argument is
that a considerable amount of "natural control" is provided for by the general way in which older persons are treated within limited temporal perspectives. "Awareness" is most centrally relevant only with patients with
whom, were staff not aware, matters like the future would be relevantly
discussed, i.e., the non-elderly.

awaiting his inheritance, or to those members of the family whose daily activities are severely restricted by the care they give their aging parent. Where the social consequences of death are taken to be of greater import, we find reference to the fact of "dying" made within more extended temporal schema of anticipation.

In the hospital setting however, "dying" takes on its central significance insofar as death is considered likely on the current admission, for it is then that the hospital, its personnel and its activities are directly involved in the affair of the death. That all very old patients are, in some more general sense of the term, "dying," is an irrelevant issue, not because of the absence or presence of "fatal diseases," but because the consequences of regarding them in that way are both immaterial from the standpoint of the hospital's activities, and, it could be argued, quite detrimental to the ideological organization of medical practice with the elderly. For physicians to assume an existential posture toward death, or operate under the auspices of an actuarial calculus, would seem to undercut the central notion that the doctor's job is to "prevent death." That the greatest proportion of very ill patients in our society are elderly, provides for the essential importance of restricting the temporal confines of predictions of death and action based upon an assessment of inevitable demise. In orienting his daily treatment activities with the elderly, the physician must develop the ability to disattend the possibility of death, unless it is quite imminent. Pessimism about life and actions based on that pessimism seem warranted, in the medical world at least, only when death becomes contemplated within the temporal confines of the hospital-doctor-patient-relative contractual relationship, and the temporally bounded contract, at County Hospital, extends little beyond the boundaries of any given hospital admission. The case of the private physician, with a different kind of contractual involvement in the affairs of his patient, within a more extended temporal matrix, is presumably quite different. Dying takes on a more extended temporal significance to the degree that the physician is more implicated into the social worlds of his patients and their families when his patients are recurrently his patients.

Appendix II

Extensions Outside the Hospital: Notes on a Sociology of Mourning

In the course of observations which were made at a funeral parlor in Miami, Florida, I observed a woman who came into the parlor director's office just prior to the beginning of a funeral ceremony to speak with the rabbi, who was busy arranging last minute details of protocol with the mortician and his staff. She introduced herself by name and as a sister of the deceased, who was a woman in her late forties with several adolescent children. As is customary in Jewish ceremonies, the rabbi was to read off a list of family members who had attended the ceremony, to be ritually presented as those who had assembled to pay their last respects to the deceased. She asked the rabbi to include her name on the list, saying "I was not at the Bar Mitzvah of the eldest" (the older boy of the deceased), this being explicitly proposed as the special reason she wanted to insure that her name be included as among those assembled for the ceremony.

I should like to suggest the sense of such a request by considering how the occasion of a death may be seen to stand, along with certain other events (births, weddings and divorces), as a happening warranting a "family roll call," and thereby as the occasion for drawing the boundaries of social units in general. My main concern shall be to try

194

to locate some of the principles which regulate the seeming manner in which the news of a death is spread to members of the "family" and others.[1] The material on which the discussion is based was drawn from conversation with members of deceased persons' families, during the period immediately following the death in the hospital, and upon some observations I managed to make during the time others were being informed of the deceased's death after relatives left the hospital setting.

At least in American society, there is, associated with any given person, a class of others, partially nameable in kinship terms, who are considered entitled to learn of a person's death in a direct fashion. For heuristic purposes I can conceive of a set of concentric rings, surrounding any person (A), each circle being distinguished from the others by a differing amount of time and medium in and by which its occupants can rightfully expect to be informed of A's death. In general, it is possible to learn a good deal about a person's position in a variety of social structures by mapping out the circles of those persons entitled to learn about his death in each of the various combinations of time and medium lapses.

The innermost circle can be said to consist of those persons who are entitled to learn of A's death in both a direct and rapid fashion. In our society this set of persons seems to consist of those who are known as members of the "immediate family," a notion which I shall explore in detail below. They have rights to know of the death very soon after it occurs, usually within moments or hours, and, it appears, (at least in the middle classes) expect to be informed either in person or over the telephone. Members of the "immediate family" regard it as improper to inform one another of a death by letter, or even telegraph

---

[1] In nearly every ethnography in which death is treated, attention is given to the way which persons use to spread news of a death through kinship and other collectivities. For an excellent detailed analysis of the "day of the death," see Goody, J., *op. cit.*, pp. 51-55.

It has been a traditional notion in anthropological theory that rituals attendant upon death reintegrate the social group. Malinowski, Durkheim, Gluckman, Hertz, Van Gennep and others have accorded central attention to the solidarity functions of *rites de passage*. My focus here is rather more limited, namely to the ways in which a death's occurrence, as a piece of reportable news, can be seen to occasion various demonstrations of group loyalties. I will not deal with funeral ceremonies themselves.

wire. If there is a proper person available to personally inform them, a son of the deceased for example expects to be personally informed, as does the wife, parent and generally, a sibling. Telegraph wires are reserved for special occasions, as when no telephone is available, and despite their urgency, they are considered neither urgent or personal enough when informing one who is especially close to the deceased. Informing a member of the immediate family in person is considered proper, it seems, only if a person can reach him rapidly, and before he might learn of the death in an improper way.

Under some circumstances, as with the deaths of presidents of nations, any person in the society may feel entitled to learn of the news rapidly, and intimate members of the family may have only a brief few moments of private access to the news, if any. While urgency of informing prevails in such circumstances, a significant difference in medium exists in the informing of "anyman" and members of the immediate family. Prominent persons' deaths may be urgently announced over the radio or television, and while that serves to rapidly inform others, it is not an especially personal way of spreading news. The radio may not be turned on and one may not hear such news before others, but unless one is a member of the immediate family or otherwise especially acquainted or close to the deceased, he cannot say "How come I wasn't *told?*" The radio or TV is not a way of "telling." Were it the case that with prominent persons' deaths all persons had a similar sort of right to know, the radio or TV would not be useable; rather, mass telegrams, or some such method would be employed. There is a significant difference in rights depending upon whether the deceased in question is merely "famous" or personally known.[2]

When a prominent person dies, or when a person dies in such circumstances that the announcement of his death might be properly made via the mass media, effort is made to contact members of the immediate family before the public-at-large is informed. Depending

[2] For a definition of *fame,* see Goffman, E., *Stigma, op. cit.,* p. 68:
. . . by the term "fame" we seem to refer to the possibility that the circle of people who know about a given individual, especially in connection with a rare desirable achievement or possession, can become very wide, and at the same time much wider than the circle of those who know him personally.

upon the particular circumstances of the death and the particular fame of the deceased, such efforts may or may not be successful. In Kennedy's death, some members of the immediate family did not learn of his death personally.[3] While airline companies refuse to release passenger lists of crashed planes before family members are personally informed, on occasion news trickles out before personal informing is completed.

If for some reason there is a concern not to inform a member of the immediate family first, in the case of prominent persons' deaths particularly, such family members must be isolated, taken away from access to the mass media.[4] When persons die, those not intimately connected with the family may feel as though they are intruders should they find themselves in a position where they learn of the death at the same time as members of the immediate family, or be in the family's presence very close to the time of the death. In one Cohen case, a person arrived at the hospital when a friend had just died, and seeing that members of the family were assembled outside their relative's room, in what appeared to be a grieving scene, quietly left without encountering them. He reported that he didn't feel comfortable being present at such a moment and would prefer to wait until a more appropriate time to express his condolences. He felt that this was a time for the family to be left alone.[5]

Sympathizers properly time their encounters with the immediately bereaved. Persons who lie on the fringe of the deceased's social circle feel some discomfort in offering condolences at a point too close to the death, feeling that such a time is properly reserved for immediate family members. In paying house visits to the immediately bereaved,

---

[3] "President Kennedy's younger sister, Rose, learned of his assassination today while watching a television broadcast from Dallas, Texas, where he was shot." *The New York Times,* November 22, 1963.

[4] When Kennedy died there was a concern not to inform his children until their mother could tell them herself. They were hurriedly secluded and kept behind closed doors all afternoon, away from public contact, until she arrived to tell them herself. See *The New York Times,* November 22, 1963, p. 4.

[5] In Kennedy's death, *The New York Times* reported:

Newsmen and photographers who were at the Hyannis Airport in Barnstable when the Senator and his sister arrived shortly before 5 P.M., apologized for having to be on hand. (November 22, 1963, p. 2)

the sympathizer likes to have some assurance that he will not be intruding upon an intimate family scene. Generally, information as to the propriety of such a visit is obtained from one who occupies a closer relationship to the immediately bereaved. Quite frequently in such situations certain persons emerge as organizers of sympathizers. They are usually those who are close enough to the immediately bereaved to be in a position to speak in their behalf on matters of protocol, yet not so close to the deceased himself as to be more properly engaged in active grieving themselves.

It is to be additionally noted that while concern is shown for the death as a "family affair," the occasion may nonetheless constitute a way in which usually operative rules of social distance are bypassed. Offers of sympathy must be accepted without invitation. That places the more distant sympathizer in a situation of ambiguity, for should he enter the family scene when only members of the family are present, he is accepted nonetheless, out of respect for his intent, and can feel that his intrusion is something the immediately bereaved cannot sanction, a fact which may make it more strainful. Immediately bereaved find themselves open to receiving persons in a more intimate and less controllable way than they ordinarily would.[6] It is apparently a custom in large sectors of our society for the immediately bereaved's house to be open in the days immediately following the death. As a counterpart, perhaps, of the wake, and in Jewish circumstances termed the period of "shiva," such occasions lack the usual rules which govern invitations. The door is left open and all comers are free to walk in and pay their respects. One finds, in such circumstances, an admixture of close relatives, close friends and mere acquaintances. Such occasions, perhaps by the very virtue of the considerable variability in perspective which participants hold with respect to the death, are known to frequently turn into sociability affairs.[7]

It can be suggested that the lack of required invitations may also work in an obverse fashion. Persons who might otherwise not be ones who could be invited, may nonetheless arrive at the funeral or the bereaved's home. It is routinely reported in newspapers that famous

[6] They are, in Goffman's terms, "open persons." See *Behavior in Public Places, op. cit.,* p. 126.

[7] This sociability may well be a function of the great number of tranquilizers taken and the amount of liquor consumed on such occasions.

persons attend funerals of "commoners," especially if the death can have some larger significance than that which it holds for the family. The Vice-President of the United States attending the funeral of a civil rights worker killed in Mississippi is such an example. He could not properly be invited to attend, and in coming therefore bestows some wider significance upon the event.

Returning to the spread of the news, it is to be seen that for some persons there may be no one to tell at all, the only people likely to be aware of the death being those various community health officials whose primary responsibility is to legally certify persons' deaths and legally dispose of human remains. On frequent occasions the only persons involved in a County Hospital death were the police, the coroner's office and staff members on the Emergency Unit. These persons stand in merely an occupationally entitled relationship to the occurrence and news of deaths.[8]

County's physicians have a conception of a proper order in considering whom to call and whom to speak to when announcing a death over the telephone. They employ a standardized conception of an order, one which is generally applicable without respect for the particular individuals involved, but for any given death. If it is a child who has died, they request to speak to the father. If the father is not available they speak to the mother and announce the death to her. If neither parent is there, they leave a message and await a call from a parent, except under the circumstance where they know in advance that there is no parent. If it is a married adult who has died, the request is made to speak to the wife or husband. If that spouse is not there, they choose one of several alternatives: 1/ If the adult who died is old and known to have elderly children, the request is made to speak to a male child, and if no male child is available, to a female child; 2/ If the adult who died has no children, the request is made to speak to a brother, sister, uncle or aunt, in that preferential order;

---

[8] It is such persons, those with no locatable families, who constitute the major population of such places as county morgues and county operated cemeteries. It is to be noted that there are generally two classes of such persons, those who lie at the bottom of the social class structure, e.g., vagrants, beggars, and the like and who have no locatable family, and those who are the end points of a kinship line, who might be nonetheless prominent, with past families the members of which they have outlived.

3/ If there is no elderly child, brother, sister, uncle or aunt, a more distant relative will be told of the death; *4/* If there is no available relative, and only under that circumstance, inquiry is made as to whether or not there is a close friend, and that person is informed. Under no circumstance was a person who announced himself as a friend told of the death before a relative was, if it was expected that a relative could be contacted, even if that meant that long distance phone calls had to be placed.

When announcing a death in face-to-face interaction, slightly different possibilities present themselves and physicians appear to have difficulty in forestalling the release of the information to some pending the arrival of others. This is equally true if the person in question insists that he learn what has happened, or appears extremely nervous. Should a relative arrive at the hospital, he will be told of the death immediately, regardless of the fact that he might lie, relative to others in the family, in a more distant formal kinship relation to the deceased. Should a friend arrive at the hospital and a relative is expected to come shortly, some effort will be made to avoid telling the friend until a relative arrives. When physicians have some control over the whereabouts of the family and can feel that a person told "out of order" will not relate the news to those entitled to hear from the doctor, they will release information to persons who otherwise would be made to wait.

Some clarification of the notion of an "announcement" is required. It is only with respect to those persons who have a "right to know" that the order of informing is relevant and with respect to whom an "announcement" must be made. Many persons in the hospital "learn" of a death because of their occupational involvement in such occurrences. And in wartime, soldiers on the battlefield "learn" of others' deaths long before members of the dead man's family do. It is only if a right to know exists that one entitled to know might not be immediately told until those having priority rights are informed. These rules have territorial boundaries. If two persons are involved in an accident and one dies, the other will be informed of his death "out of order" if he is on the scene. (It is noteworthy that persons often seek elaborative news of a death from those who are in close proximity to the person who died, and persons who have been in close proximity often feel obliged to render a more personal service to those who will otherwise learn of the death only more formally.[9])

Members of the deceased's family have the concern to spread news of his death in line with their conceptions of a proper order of information release. On the basis of my conversations with bereaved families and the few opportunities I had to observe their behavior after they left the hospital, I can begin to sketch what some of these considerations look like and provide at least a first approximation to how they were handled. Because of the limited number of cases on which the remarks below are based (I followed three families into the home after the death and spent some time with the members of one family who did their telephone calling from the hospital itself), they are to be regarded as only of the most preliminary and speculative character.

The families I witnessed seemed to be concerned that certain others learn of the deceased's death rapidly, while others need be told only later, and that any given other be informed by one who stood, vis-a-vis the deceased, in a similar formal relationship to the prospective recipient.

In one case when a man died, his wife and son arrived at the hospital shortly after the time of the death, and they were informed of it by the family physician. There were two other sons, living in different parts of the country, a daughter living in the same city, several brothers and sisters dispersed throughout the United States. Additionally, there was a large cohort of more distant relatives, friends, business associates, and neighbors. In making decisions as to whom to call, in what order and by whom, the following considerations seemed

---

[9] Apparently when persons such as "wartime buddies" announce deaths to members of the deceased's family, they feel obliged to warrant their own interest in delivering the news, and their right to be doing so, by referring to the intimate character of their past relation to the deceased, as is seen in the following fictional example:

> I know you will hear the news from the Army, but I am writing to you because Roger wanted me to tell you if anything happened to him. He wanted his wife to hear about him from a friend and I am a friend. I am also Jewish and I tell you this so you will understand that there was a bond between me and Roger because of that. Roger didn't tell many people he was a Jew.

Giovannitti, L., *The Prisoners of Combine D,* (New York: Bantam Books), 1959, pp. 278-279.

to be operative. The sons and daughters should be informed first, and the son at the hospital proposed that he call one of the sons, have that son call the other, and then he would call the daughter, the expressed concern being with speed; to one son he said, "Will you call Julius while I call Susan." A further instruction, "After you call Julius, will you call Uncle Harry and have Julius call Aunt Sylvia, and I'll call Uncle Sam and Aunt Beatrice," seemed to arrange the news spread so that the brothers and sisters would be informed all at approximately the same time. It was felt that sisters and brothers ought not be told before sons and daughters. This was true in all cases I observed except one, where the son in question was a young boy; these rules regarding rights to know and orders of informing seem to hold only if adult recipients are involved. Sisters and brothers were to be told by sons and daughters. An additional consideration, present in several witnessed cases, was that the sex of the recipient was relevant to the manner of news spread. Before placing a call to an aunt, the son's mother (the widow) suggested: "Ask for Paul first and tell him" (Paul being the aunt's husband, the deceased's brother-in-law). When a son at the hospital told the other son to call another sister of the deceased, he instructed, "Why don't you try to reach Sam at work and let him break the news" (Sam being another brother-in-law).

It appears improper to have a relative of one kin-class, say children, brothers-sisters, aunts-uncles or cousins, be told of the death of a relative by a member of a kin-class more "distant," formally speaking, from the deceased. This rule seems to hold strongly for the first few sets, children, brothers-sisters, aunts-uncles, whereafter distinctions between first and second cousins seemed less important. A brother would not inform another brother or sister of their brother's death by having a cousin call him or her, though a son or daughter can properly call a brother or sister, and a brother can call a cousin. There is apparently an operative rule that members of kin-classes not be told of the death by nonkin. While friends were occasionally told before some of the relatives were, they were neither instructed nor felt properly situated to inform family members of the death.

An interesting fact about the order of informing is that it seemed typical for the closest of relatives to the deceased to play very little part in the dissemination of news. In all the cases I observed, and in additional conversations with persons about their own experiences in such situations, I found that wives and husbands of deceased persons did not inform others. Generally, if there are sons or daughters, they informed one another of a parent's death, and widows or widowers did not. In two hospital cases the widow requested to have the physician inform a child of the father's death. In one case in which a young woman died, the husband asked the physician to call her father and tell him of his daughter's death.

In spreading news rapidly to others, informers have the concern not to tell others of the death with a degree of urgency and implied shock value inordinately greater (or less) than is warranted by their presumed emotional attachment to the deceased. An urgent delivery of news of a death says something to the recipient about how it is assumed he stood relative to the deceased, and requires of him that he respond in kind.[10] To be awakened in the midst of night with news that someone has died, implies that considerable value has been attributed to the relationship between the recipient and the deceased, or the relationship between the immediately bereaved and the recipient.

It is important to note that a consideration in releasing news of a death is that simultaneous with the concern to let those who knew the deceased well be informed rapidly of his death is the concern to inform those closely related to the immediately bereaved, whether or not they are close to the deceased. Bereavement seems to involve as much grieving over the other's loss as over the loss itself, though characteristically different kinds of interests are at stake in the two instances. With respect to most persons, one can find that at some point the import of their death changes in character, for recipients, from a loss those recipients themselves feel to a loss they feel others feel. Deaths have a way of being located as particularly tied to certain persons. So it is said "She lost her mother," "Did you hear about Mrs. Jones' husband?", "They lost a child last year." We can notice in

---

10 Just as a casual announcement of death implies some degree of alienation from the one who died, and, on occasion, disrespect for such relationships as that which obtained between the person and the deceased. Camus provides a classic example of a nonchalant announcement:

> When we had dressed, she stared at my black tie and asked if I was in mourning. I explained that my mother had died. "When?" she asked, and I said, "Yesterday." She made no remark, though I thought she shrank away a little.

The Stranger, (New York: Vintage Books), 1958, p. 24.

examining the way news of a death is disseminated, that members of the "immediate family"—brothers, sisters, sons, daughters, spouses, parents—are taken to attend the death as their own loss, and while concern for the welfare of one closest the deceased may be strongly evidenced, each member of the "immediate family" is taken to have suffered a personal loss by virtue of the death. They are all, to some extent, newly bereaved persons. As the news spreads from kin to friends, business associates, and neighbors it becomes posed as a loss which has occurred for the family, and while such more distant recipients might experience a deep sense of personal loss, they are less likely to feel entitled to regard themselves as in grief. While one can say "a very close friend of mine died," in some sense he lacks that bona fide status as a bereaved which one for whom the tie is based on the person's status as a member of the "immediate family" has.

The "immediate family" can be said to consist of that set of persons who are entitled to a "nonqualified use of my" as a way of describing their relationship to the deceased, where that usage can be employed as a way of warrantably asserting their rights to treatments as having suffered a loss. By a "nonqualified use of my," I intend to refer to the circumstance where one need not add, for example, such descriptive qualifiers such as "good," "best" and "dear" as required ways of proposing the sense of the death and entitlement to bereaved status. The son may properly say "my father died" and have that assertion warrant others' treatments of him as bereaved, without it necessary that he employ an adjectival qualification, e.g., "my good father," "the father whom I loved so much," etc.[11] While others may and do employ "my," those who are not members of what appears to be taken as the "immediate family" seem required, to warrant the death as their loss, to engage in qualificatory descriptive work. The sheer announcement a "relative of mine died" does not seem to warrant treatment as a bereaved, nor does "my friend died," or "my sister's husband's niece died." In our society, there is only a delimited class of persons who may properly receive treatments as bereaved without providing descriptive accounts of the character of their relation to the deceased. For

---

[11] There is a usage, the "beloved mother" which appears almost exclusively in newspaper notices and ceremonies of death. Rather than being a required qualification, the term "beloved" here seems to be a way in which special respect is shown the dead.

those who must provide such accounts, entitlement to bereavement is rather weak. Furthermore, the immediate family is not defined as coextensive with a formally defined kin network, for only persons who are spouses, siblings, children and parents seem to have legitimate use of the nonqualified "my." [12]

Persons for whom the mere announcement of a relational category does not unqualifiedly provide their status as bereaved, occasionally engage in efforts to class themselves as having had essentially similar relations to the deceased as those had by proper "my" users. So we characteristically encounter descriptive phrases such as "she was like a mother to me," and "we were like brothers." These "category-linked" descriptions can be seen as efforts to claim at least quasi-bereaved status where a formal position does not lend itself to such rights. Several possible uses of these ways of talking can be tentatively suggested. Their use seems to be a particularly powerful way of expressing grief. In contrast to expressions of sympathy which involve one in an enumeration of the features of the deceased which "made him such a wonderful person" or of the features of the "close relationship we had," the mere announcement of the fact that he stands as a "brother" suffices to establish or propose the sense of the loss. In situations of offering sympathy, persons in so describing their regard for the deceased attempt to show their respect for the bereaved via the fact that they claim a similar relation to the deceased, and thereby have understanding of the event's significance for the immediately bereaved. The usage is a particularly strong conversational device, the citation of the category being a more adequate way of summarizing one's feeling and also a way of being able to avoid having to mention any specific feelings. The circumstance of a death nicely provides persons with the opportunity for demonstrating their closeness to some social world, via their portrayals of a relationship with the deceased, which could not be as readily demonstrated were the deceased around and potentially able to disaffirm such claims as to the "belonging" of the person in question. The dead can no longer speak for themselves,

[12] The hospital nursing manual on regulations on absences for a family death stated:

Three days are granted for death of an immediate family member. Immediate family is interpreted as husband, wife, son, daughter, mother or father of the employee. One day is allowed for the death of other relatives.

so claims of past intimacies can be made which would otherwise only be assertable with more attention to the person's possible presence. The opportunity to express grief is an opportunity for the expression of intimacy which the griever might not otherwise ever have.

It was noted that, formally speaking, members of the immediate family do not, themselves, spread news of the person's death to those more distant. Insofar as the death is located as their loss, members of the immediate family, in announcing its occurrence to those for whom it does not constitute such a loss, may be seen by others to be soliciting sympathy. There is apparently the concern to sustain the impression that gestures of sympathy are genuinely given, and emanate from the sympathizer's respect and sense of concern for the family's welfare which he, without an apparent sense of obligation, felt upon learning of the death. For the immediately bereaved to impart news of a death is in effect for him to announce his own status as a bereaved, and in so doing he may directly enforce an attitude of sympathy in the other without letting it be naturally exhibited. The recipient is placed in the position of having to produce sympathy on the spot, and that, in turn, may deprive gestures of sympathy of one of their central powers, the sense, at least, that they are genuinely offered. When a death occurs, much may be at stake for the family as regards the degree of sympathy which the community evidences. The family's status, the achievements of the deceased, the circle of his acquaintances and friends and his degree of regard by others are matters which are taken to be significantly tested by such indices as the number of persons who heard about the death, how many came to the funeral, how many sympathy cards and phone calls were received. These concerns can be of paramount significance to members of the family. A "poor turnout" can be, in many instances, as hard a fact to live with as the death itself.[13] While

---

[13] It is to be noted that any of the features of a "good turnout" can be systematically handled by those who do not want to have the funeral so used. Families who are sure about their own position can insist upon a "private funeral," request that no flowers be sent. Families who might have reason to be troubled about what a funeral turnout might show as regards the deceased's actual esteem, can similarly protect themselves, for in restricting the funeral to a private one they prohibit its being used as a testing ground. And lastly, those whose esteem was questionable can be made to seem greatly respected by purposefully maximizing the turnout. Gangsters' funerals with dozens of cars of flowers are notable examples. For a dis-

members of the family have strong expectations that others will come to exhibit their respect for the family and the deceased, the solicitation of sympathy, by independent action on the part of close family members, can weaken the presumed meaning of sympathy.

Persons who wish to retain their rights to have others treat them as having suffered a loss, and as thereby entitled to treatment as bona fide bereavers, refrain from taking the task of spreading news of the death, with the exception that immediate members of the family can inform one another of their common loss. The son who calls an uncle to relate his father's death, does not expectably receive "I'm sorry to hear" as a response, but should he call the neighbor, employer or friend such a response would be enforced directly. There is an additional sense in which he who relates such news, particularly if he does so to those persons in face whom he cannot, without making them very uncomfortable, show signs of pronounced grief, in some way renounces his own claim to the event's deep significance to him. Those deeply upset by a death are taken to be emotionally incapable of mustering enough composure to spread news to those less intimately involved members of the community and are taken to be in family seclusion. Not only does a person enforce an attitude of sympathy in another when announcing the death of someone close to himself to someone for whom the death has no such great meaning, but he also, it seems, detracts from the sense that he himself is deeply hurt, a sense better maintained if others can regard him as in seclusion with fellow family grievers.

From my preliminary observations, it seems that news spreads in such a fashion that at each level, persons of essentially the same formal distance from the deceased, inform one another of the death. Friends tell other friends, business associates other business associates, acquaintances tell acquaintances. In spreading news to non-family persons, the immediately bereaved generally rely on a snowballing effect by selecting certain key persons to tell so that the news will flow outwardly, following a natural ordering based on the relations between persons surrounding the deceased. If there is a set of business associates, by

---

cussion of the private funeral in the context of changing American values on ceremonies, and a general analysis of the uses of funerals, see Mandelbaum, D., "Social Uses of Funeral Rites," in Fulton, R. *op. cit.,* especially pages 356-59.

selecting one most familiar with the deceased, the immediately bereaved can leave to him the problem of telling those who should
know. They employ the knowledge that the deceased's acquaintances
know one another within certain subsets of persons, and that ones
chosen from these subsets will inform others within it. Moreover they
select as those to be informed quickly, persons who are taken to have
the best knowledge of who, within a given domain of others, would
want to know of the death, and they select persons who are likely to
know a large circle of the deceased's friends and acquaintances.

The occurrence of a death is generally regarded as something which
occurs as a unit event, as a happening of the group. That deaths are
so conceived is seen in such paradigmatic phrases as "the nation
mourns its loss," "the world lost a leader in the death of . . . ,"
"death struck their doorstep," the "family lost a son in the war," and
others. Characteristically, in announcing deaths, offering sympathies
and describing the deaths of others, relational categories and the
collections of such categories are conversationally employed; "I'm
sorry to hear about your father's death," "his brother died," "closed
because of a death in the family." In conceiving deaths as unit
affairs, a powerful basis for the enforcement of rights and responsibilities associated with the death of a unit member is thereby provided for, namely, that those rights can become linked to a member's
status as a member. Persons who are members of the unit, but
do not properly respect their responsibilities and exercise their rights,
can have their status as members jeopardized. This fact can be
variously used. Those who consider themselves disaffected from some
unit can, by declining to accept their responsibilities and exercise their
rights upon the death of a unit member, demonstrate their lack of
regard for the unit and their own membership in it.[14] The fact of the

---

[14] So, for example, when Kennedy died, the Chinese Communists did not
send a representative to the funeral, refusing to acknowledge their membership in a world for which his death was taken as an event. See *The
New York Times,* November 25, 1963, p. 1.

The way deaths are treated as unit events is clearly seen in the fact that
to do damage to a unit, killing one of its members can be an especially
powerful device. In the South today, it is reported, "white man kills
Negro," such occurrences being attacks on the entire race and not a particular Negro. It is of course well known that the murder of a unit member can be taken as an assault upon the entire unit; not a few wars have
been so started.

linkage between rights, responsibilities and membership status can also be employed by members of some unit as a way of telling others that those others are not regarded as bona fide members, by not granting them those privileges which unit members enjoy. This latter possibility constitutes a key basis for the manner in which news of a death is released.

A first way in which unit boundaries are relevantly tested by a death regards the rules governing release of news. On occasions such as deaths, persons take it that something of a census-taking occurs, whereby members of some unit go through a list of the unit's members, and inform each of them of the occurrence. In important respects, deaths are like births, divorces and weddings in that each of these "census events" is taken to involve some sort of roll call procedure, whereby a set of others is notified or invited. For a person not to be notified of such an occurrence, should he take it that he is a member of a unit for which the occurrence could be taken to have some topical significance, e.g., as a unit affair itself, as a piece of gossip, or whatever, and should he take it that a procedure was undertaken whereby certain of the unit's members systematically engaged in informing others of the occurrence, he has a way of seeing that he has specifically "not been informed." While announcements of death occur regularly in the obituary column of the newspaper, readers of the paper generally do not formulate the notion that they have not been informed of listed persons' deaths. Should a reader have the conception that he is a member of some unit, other members of which, prior to the placing of the obituary, personally informed, in a systematic fashion, a collection of other unit members, then he has available a resource for seeing that he was not notified.

In the case of deaths, a prominent unit is the "family." The "family" is attended as the locus of obligations and rights surrounding the death of one of its members. Persons who regard themselves as "family members," taking it that a systematic procedure for notification was employed in spreading news of a member's death, can thereby have a way of seeing whether or not they were "told." It is by reference to the category "family" that one can locate his own absence, and it is by reference to that category that persons decide who is to be informed in the case of a death.

The category "family" is not to be taken as coextensive with that entire set of paired relational categories which can be named in kinship terms, but rather has a much more delimited meaning. What elderly grandparents conceive of as the "family" may substantially differ from that conception held by young adult members. It seems generally true that the elderly members of a kinship structure have a much more extended definition of the "family" than do younger members. In one Cohen instance there was an argument between the son of a deceased woman and his father over who should be notified of her death. The son restricted his calls to members of the immediate family, and the father urged him to see to it that a whole line of cousins were informed. The son pointed out that such persons would learn but that it wasn't their place to call.

In spreading news of a death it seemed to be a first consideration that those persons be informed who, were they not to be informed, would be able to see that they were specifically bypassed, and would have available a way of assigning responsibility to the "family" for having ignored them. What seems to happen is that the spread of news operates within "accountable units," where, for each unit "immediate members of the family," "distant relations," "business associates," "friends," delivery of the news of the death can stand as an event which has import for the recipient's membership status in the unit. Throughout the period of time in which the families I observed made their phone calls, remarks on the order of the following were made: "Uncle Sam would be hurt if we didn't call him right away"; "Shouldn't we call Mr. G?"; "Mr. H. will tell him, I'm sure"; "Would you tell Harry to tell Ethel to tell the people at the store?"; "How about that cousin in New Jersey, the Schwartz?" "He's Julius' boy, let Julius tell him." One could observe, via a stopwatch, the process of news spread to each of a successive level of kin and nonkin recipients. The social structure could be "timed."

Merely "finding out" is not sufficient, for in not being specifically informed by the right party, or in finding out only incidentally, persons have a way of seeing that what they took to be their own ranking in the unit is obviously not so regarded. Among a collection of mutual friends, persons rank their own standing relative to each other, such that C might consider himself closer to the deceased friend than that person from whom he received news of the death. Should that occur, and should C take it that A and B knew of the death, and informed E, F and G, he could see, in learning from those more removed than he regarded himself, that he had been bypassed. When persons related to the deceased might be independent of one another and if the set of friends were not a "set" but merely some number of unrelated persons, such an inferential basis would be absent. In such a circumstance of nonconnectedness one might properly learn of the death in only an incidental fashion.

The remark of the women in the mortician's study evidences the fact that such unit events can have a major function in their boundary-testing possibilities. Apparently there is a sense in which such occasions can be additive or substitutable, so that having missed one a person can, by attending another, have his membership nonetheless retained.[15] From this perspective, a death's occurrence can be said to merely occasion the expression of group loyalties, and becomes somewhat interchangeable with a variety of other happenings. Among some persons for whom the exchange of gossip is the predominant basis of a relationship, any piece of gossip can equally serve to occasion a demonstration of the intactness of the relationship. That a death might have a similarly occasioned function for some is an interesting possibility.

I pointed out above that members of the "immediate family" tell one another of the death but do not tell others, that constituting a possibility that sympathy will be seen as being solicited and an activity inappropriate for one who must appear deeply upset. There are a set of persons who stand in a special sort of marginal relationship to the deceased and an "immediate relationship" to the bereaved. Among such persons, the death can be posed as having its central significance in that it is an event which is located as having occurred for the immediately bereaved and not themselves. Persons so located, the children of a man whose sister has died, for example, have their entitlement to learn based upon their relationship not necessarily to the deceased, but to the immediately bereaved. It is likely that a father will announce to his son the death of his wife's sister, and the mother will announce to the son the death of his father's sibling. In each case (and this practice was observed in two cases in the hospital), the announcer and recipient do not stand in such a relationship that the recipient would

---

[15] There seems to be a hierarchical organization to such events however, so that missing a funeral can be significantly more disastrous than, say, forgetting a birthday or a wedding.

properly offer condolences to the announcer. This seems to be generally true at each point in the dissemination of the news, with the exception that key marginal figures, those who are in "attending" relations to the bereaved, i.e., those for whom the immediately bereaved are, for themselves, centrally located, but are not immediately bereaved themselves, often serve as informational bridges between the immediately bereaved and other recipients. For example, should a husband learn of his sibling's death before his wife does, in relating that news to her, sympathy is properly offered him. With the exception of that special sort of encounter, the news is then distributed within classes of persons where exchanges of sympathy, between announcer and recipient, would not be properly expected.